Powerhouse

An Intermediate Business English Course

Peter Strutt

LONGMAN

Addison Wesley Longman Limited
Edinburgh Gate, Harlow, Essex CM20 2JE, England
and associated companies throughout the world.

© Addison Wesley Longman Limited 1998

The right of Peter Strutt to be identified as the author of this work has been asserted
by him in accordance with the Copyright, Designs and Patents Act 1988.

All rights reserved; no part of this publication may be reproduced, stored in a retrieval system,
or transmitted in any form or by any means, electronic, mechanical, photocopying, recording
or otherwise, without the prior written permission of the Publishers.

Published by Addison Wesley Longman Ltd 1998.

Set in $10\frac{1}{2}$/ 13pt Adobe Garamond.

Printed in Spain by Graficas Estella.

Produced for the publishers by de Henseler Books.

Designed by Oxprint Design, Oxford.

ISBN 0582 32560 9

Acknowledgements
We are grateful to Hitachi Home Electronics (Europe) Limited for consenting to the use of
the title 'Powerhouse'.

We are grateful to the following for permission to reproduce copyright material:
Arrow Books Ltd for an adapted extract from *THE AGE OF UNREASON* by Charles Handy;
Cadbury Ltd for text and images from *CADBURY'S WEBSITE PAGE* (http://www.cadburyco.uk);
Dow Jones & Co Inc for an adapted extract from 'AOL's E-Mail Service is Brought Down by Soft
Ware Bug in Third Large Outage' by Rebecca Quick in the *WALL SRTEET JOURNAL*, 26.11.97;
The Economist Newspaper Ltd for an adapted extract from 'The music of the metropolis' in *THE
ECONOMIST* 2.8.97 and an extract from 'Puzzling failure of economics' in *THE ECONOMIST*
23.8.97; The Financial Times Ltd for an adapted extract from 'NVT: A better use of time?' in
THE FINANCIAL TIMES 10.11.97; Guardian News Services Ltd for an abridged and simplified
extract from 'Trampling on the children' by Julia Finch in *THE GUARDIAN* 12.9.97 and an
abridged extract from 'Business: At the altar of the Machine ...' by Charles Handy in *THE
OBSERVER* 31.8.97; Random House UK Ltd for an abridged extract from *MAVERICK* by
Rocardo Semler, Arrow Books, 1994; John Wiley & Sons Inc for an adapted extract from
DO'S AND TABOOS OF HOSTING INTERNATIONAL VISITORS by Robert E Axell.

The publisher would like to thank and acknowledge the following sources for pictures reproduced
on the following pages:
Advertising Archives: 31; Arrow: 73; The Guardian: 65, 70; Gill Metcalfe: 33; Matthew Morgan: 4
(1–4), 30; Pictor: 7, 12, 16, 37, 38, 39, 41, 48l, 69; Popperfoto: 61 (5); Rex Features: 49, 60, 61a,
61 (1–4), 71; Telegraph Colour Library: 5, 12, 17, 25, 49, 52–53, 54, 64; Topham: 48r.

Illustrated by John Martin & Artists, David Mostyn and Oxprint Design, Oxford.

contents

1 connections

JOB DESCRIPTIONS   Using the information from these cards, write about each person.

personnel

Name	Anne Patel
Company	Greshams
Position	*Attorney*
Current project	Investigation of allegations of insider trading

Name	Jacob Kastor
Company	RGA International Ltd
Position	*Human Resources Manager*
Current project	Implementation of quality assessment procedures

DELTACOM

Name	Carol Farih
Company	DELTACOM
Position	*Marketing Co-ordinator*
Current project	Launch of new range of up-market products

Argenton plc

- **NAME** Jean-Marie Barrault
- **COMPANY** Argenton plc
- **POSITION** *Financial Manager*
- **CURRENT PROJECT** Preparation of next year's budget

1   Anne Patel works as an attorney for Greshams. At the moment, she is investigating allegations of insider trading.

2

3

4

MODERN BRITAIN   Complete the article using the present continuous tense.

British cities [1] _are booming_ (boom) again thanks to a reviving economy. London's economy [2] .... (grow) twice as fast as the nation's as a whole. A range of London-based economies, from finance to the theatre to fashion, [3] .... (expand). Elsewhere, city centres have become huge building sites. Newcastle [4] .... (embark) on a £120m ($195m) reconstruction of its city centre, Sunderland [5] .... (build) a new leisure complex, Bristol [6] .... (rebuild) its docklands and Birmingham [7] .... (pull down) its ugly Bull Ring inner-city shopping centre. From Coventry to Glasgow the shops are full, restaurants are crowded, house prices [8] .... (rise) and jobs are on offer.

The Economist, *2 August 1997*

A PHONE BOX   **1**   Complete the conversation by changing the verbs in brackets into either the present simple or the present continuous. (One of the verbs can be used in either tense – which one?)

YVONNE   Hello.

MARTIN   Is that you, Yvonne?

YVONNE   Er ... yes.

MARTIN   Hi!

YVONNE   Martin? Is that you, Martin? What a surprise!

Where [1] _are you ringing_ (you/ring) from?

MARTIN   I'm in a phone box in Cambridge.

YVONNE   What [2] .... (you/do) in England? I thought you were in Italy.

MARTIN   I was, but I [3] .... (attend) a conference in London tomorrow and so Maria and I [4] .... (stay) with some friends here.

YVONNE   Great! Is Maria with you now?

MARTIN   No. She [5] .... (do) some shopping.

You [6] .... (know) Maria, every time we [7] .... (come) to Cambridge she [8] .... (spend) hours in bookshops.

YVONNE   Yes, I [9] .... (remember) the last time we went shopping together. Martin, how long [10] .... (you/plan) to stay?

MARTIN   Until Sunday afternoon.

YVONNE   Well, look, we [11] .... (have) a dinner party Friday evening. Why don't you come over and join us?

MARTIN   Yeah, sure, we'd love to. Any particular time?

YVONNE   Let's say 8 for 8.30. We never [12] .... (eat) before then.

MARTIN   OK, great. We'll see you on Friday.

2   [cassette icon] Listen and check your answers.

■ *For more on the present tenses, go to page 141 of the Course Book.* ■

1 🔲 Listen to the two phone conversations and fill in each Post-it® with the information you hear.

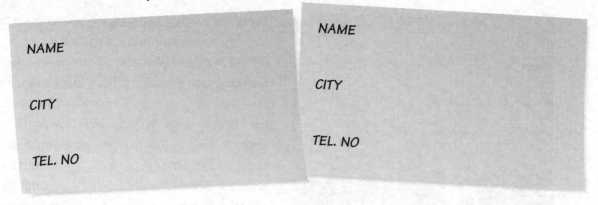

NAME

CITY

TEL. NO

NAME

CITY

TEL. NO

2 🔲 Listen to the two phone conversations and fill in each message pad with the information you hear.

Message From

Name

Company

Urgent ☐
Can Wait ☐ (tick appropriate box)

Tel. No.

Message From

Name

Company

Urgent ☐
Can Wait ☐ (tick appropriate box)

Tel. No.

PHONE WORDS

Use the words in the box to make telephone expressions.

Example:

switchboard operator, long distance call

switchboard   *distance*

phone

call   *conference*

toll

number

operator   *collect*

long   *card*   *free*

A PHONE JUMBLE   Three people are involved in this jumbled conversation: Michael Sullivan of Global Engines, Bill Gould of Parsons Engineering and a receptionist.

1 Put the conversation into the correct order.

☐ Right. Well, thank you for your call.

1 Parsons Engineering. Can I help you?

☐ Yes, they've just been dispatched by DCL Courier. They should be with you by tomorrow morning. If there's any problem, then just get back to me.

☐ I'm afraid he's on another line at the moment. Would you like to hold or can I take a message?

☐ Hello. My name is Michael Sullivan of Global Engines. I've been trying to get through to you. I'm calling to find out whether the spare parts I ordered last week have been sent off.

☐ Mr Gould is free now. I'm putting you through.

☐ No, it doesn't matter. I'll hold.

☐ Hello, this is Michael Sullivan of Global Engines. Could I speak to Mr Gould in Customer Services, please?

☐ Thank you. Goodbye.

☐ Oh good. Yes, OK, but I hope it won't be necessary.

☐ Hello. Bill Gould.

2 📼 Listen and check your answers.

THE ALPHABET   Write the letters of the alphabet which are pronounced with the vowel sounds underlined in each word.

Example:

h<u>e</u>lp /e/   *F, M, N, S, X*

1 sp<u>ea</u>k /i:/   ....

2 l<u>i</u>ne /aɪ/   ....

3 h<u>o</u>ld /əʊ/   ....

4 w<u>ai</u>t /eɪ/   ....

5 thr<u>ough</u> /u:/   ....

6 ch<u>ar</u>ge /ɑ:/   ....

CULTURE AND COMMUNICATION

In his book *Do's and Taboos of Hosting International Visitors*, the American writer Roger E. Axtell begins with three true stories.

Complete each story by choosing the ending (*a*, *b* or *c*) that you think is printed in the book.

1 In Grand Rapids, Larry Bratschie, Marketing Executive for a large manufacturer of office furniture, once hosted a key group of Japanese customers. Knowing that the Japanese were great gift-givers, Bratschie purchased silver pocket knives for each guest. He had them carefully wrapped Japanese-style (pastel coloured paper, no bows) and positioned at each place at the dining table. As the Japanese opened their gifts, each guest suddenly went silent. Each carefully put the knife back in the box and stared into the distance. As the guests left the dinner table, the gifts remained behind, untouched. Later Bratschie learnt that in the Japanese culture

a it is an insult to receive the same gift as everyone else.

b the act of presenting a knife as a gift can be a symbol of suicide.

c knives have strong sexual connotations.

2 C. Edward Boggs of Bluefield, West Virginia hosted his West German distributor and his wife. Wanting to make a good impression, he ordered a dozen red roses and had them placed in their hotel room. Unknown to Boggs

a giving red roses to a German woman may have strong romantic associations.

b red roses are considered to bring bad luck and only bought for funerals.

c the number twelve is a symbol of hostility in German culture.

3 When a delegation of buyers from the People's Republic of China came to Nashville, export executive Ken Kirkpatrick arranged for VIP treatment. At the welcoming dinner, he ordered the best cuts of American ribs of beef. As is the custom in most fine American restaurants, the beef was served rare. The Chinese took one look at the meat, blanched and refused to touch it. Kirkpatrick quickly discovered that

a they were afraid of mad cow disease.

b they were totally unaccustomed to rare red meat.

c it is unacceptable to eat beef when doing business.

ETIQUETTE Complete the passage with the words in the box.

ceremony **threatening** formal bows avoid

If you need to do business with the Japanese, it's a good idea to learn some etiquette. It helps to be [1] *formal*............... rather than relaxed.

If your Japanese counterpart [2] .... to you, don't try to do the same – just nod your head a little. The exchange of business cards (*meishi*) is an important [3] .... ; if you write on them, you will cause offence.

When you begin to deal with the Japanese, remember that they don't like to negotiate face-to-face. They find it too confrontational and in their society [4] .... it wherever possible.

Control your gestures and keep your hands by your sides because the Japanese find big arm movements [5] .... Speak slowly and keep your voice calm and even.

SOCIAL CONVENTIONS

Here are some social 'rules' concerning behaviour in countries with a predominantly Anglo-American culture. Choose the best behaviour to adopt in each case.

1 When you meet someone for the first time,
  a it is normal to shake hands with them.
  b you give a small bow.
  c you kiss them on the cheek.
  d you hug them.

2 When you are invited to someone's house for dinner,
  a it is normal to arrive half an hour early.
  b you must be on time.
  c it is normal to arrive ten minutes late.
  d you can bring a friend with you.

3 When a person is sitting alone at a table in a bar,
  a you can sit down at the same table if you ask permission.
  b you should not sit down next to them if there is another table free.
  c it depends on whether it's a man or a woman.
  d it depends on how old he or she is.

4 When there is a queue,
  a it is normal for foreigners to go to the front.
  b you have to wait in line.
  c women have to go to the back.

5 Someone sneezes. What could you say?
  a 'God be with you.'
  b 'Bless you.'
  c 'Cheers.'

6 When you take a taxi,
  a you normally give the driver a tip.
  b you never give the driver a tip.
  c you can deduct 10% from the fare.

7 Someone says 'Thank you' to you. What could you say?
  a 'You're welcome.'
  b 'Thank you.'
  c 'And the same to you.'

8 Someone asks you 'Do you mind if I smoke?' What could you say?
  a 'Yes, I don't mind.'
  b 'I'd rather you didn't.'
  c 'No, thank you very much.'

9 A colleague has heard she has been promoted. What could you say?
  a 'Congratulations.'
  b 'Good luck!'
  c 'Well made!'

10 You are in a bar and would like to buy someone a drink. What could you say?
  a 'Do you drink?'
  b 'It's your round.'
  c 'What are you having?'

TYPES OF ORGANISATION

Read the clues and write the words in the spaces provided. (Each box represents a letter.)

Clues

1 Another word for a company. _Firm_

2 Exxon, Nestlé and Unilever are all _____.

3 The first word in the abbreviation *plc*. _____

4 The second word in the abbreviation *plc*. _____

5 An American word for a large firm. _____

6 They're neither big, nor small, just a _____-sized firm.

1	F	i	r	m										
2														
3														
4														
5														
6														

SCORE: 5

PRESENT SIMPLE / PRESENT CONTINUOUS

Underline the correct form of the present.

1 I'm sorry, Mrs Grant is not available at the moment; she (speaks / <u>is speaking</u>) to a customer.

2 She (belongs / is belonging) to a union.

3 Canon (makes / is making) a wide range of photocopiers.

4 She (thinks / is thinking) of getting a transfer to another department.

5 My boss (thinks / is thinking) I should take work home at the weekend.

6 Society (changes / is changing) from a production-based economy to one based on knowledge and information.

■ *For more on the present tenses, go to page 141 of the Course Book.* ■

SCORE: 5

TELEPHONE LANGUAGE   Fill in the blanks with equivalent expressions.

hang up   get through   put you through

cut off   hold on   collect   afraid

back   leave   up   busy

1   I'm trying to connect you.   I'm trying to *put you through*.

2   We've been disconnected.   We've been _____.

3   I can't connect to the number.   I can't _____.

4   I'll put down the receiver now.   I'll _____ now.

5   Would you like to wait?   Would you like to _____?

6   The number's engaged.   The number's _____.

7   I'm sorry, he's on another line.   I'm _____ he's on another line.

8   Can you speak more loudly?   Can you speak _____?

9   Could you call again later?   Could you call _____ later?

10 Can I give you a message?   Can I _____ a message?

11 I'd like the person I'm calling   I'd like to make a _____ call.
    to pay for this call.

SCORE: 10

SOCIAL SKILLS   Match the introductions and questions with the appropriate responses.

1   How do you do?   a   A bit hectic at the moment, I'm afraid.

2   I'm sorry, we haven't been introduced.   b   That's right! How did you know my name?

3   How are things?   c   No, we've never been formally introduced.

4   Pleased to meet you.   d   No, that's right. My name's Annette Carducci.

5   You must be Michiyo Nakamoto.   e   How do you do?

6   I don't think you've met Mr Mersch before. f   I'm glad to meet you, too.

SCORE: 5

TOTAL: 25

2 the **company**

In *The Age of Unreason*, Charles Handy said that a firm was like a shamrock. The first leaf represents the core workers, the second represents specialists and the self-employed, the third symbolises the flexible labour force.

Later in the book, Handy says that there is a fourth group, the customer, who also does work for the firm.

1 Read this extract which compares the situation for the customer in the past and the present. Then fill in the table.

We now pick up our own groceries from the shelves where my parents had shop assistants to do it for them. Our own private cars have taken over from delivery vans. Furniture makers persuade us that it is clever to put up our own kitchen cabinets. Banks long ago worked out that if they could persuade customers to fill in their own deposit slips they, the banks, not the customers, would save millions. Now we also draw out our own money from their 'holes in the wall' and call it our convenience.

Smart restaurants may one day charge customers for cooking their own food where they now only, in fast food outlets, take it away and provide their own eating space. 'Help yourself' in clothes stores, supermarkets, drug stores and wine shops has turned out to be a clever way of saving labour under the label of customer preference.

Extract from The Age of Unreason *by Charles Handy*

IN THE PAST	NOW
Shop assistants served customers.	***We now pick up our own groceries from the shelves.***
Shops delivered goods to our homes.	
We had furniture made for us.	
The bank cashier filled in our deposit slips.	
Cashiers gave us our money over the counter.	

2 What prediction does Handy make for the future?

THE DOUGHNUT

Later in the book, Handy uses another metaphor – the doughnut. The heart of the doughnut represents the clearly-defined core tasks that make up a job description.

However, many jobs require the employee to take on extra work, to show initiative and do more than the basic job description. This area of activity is represented by the ring of the doughnut.

Define your own area of core responsibility and add the initiatives that are your own. Choose from those suggested in the box and add any others you can think of.

lead a team   make financial decisions   hire and fire personnel

improve quality   improve efficiency

take work home with me   keep colleagues informed

work closely with suppliers

set up my own performance targets   arrive at work as early as possible

IN MY POST I HAVE TO ...	I DON'T HAVE TO BUT I MAKE IT MY BUSINESS TO ...

WORD BUILDING

Complete the phrases with the adjectives of the words.

Example:

manager	a	_managerial_	position
1 tradition	a	....	company
2 success	a	....	firm
3 flexibility	a	....	labour force
4 secretary		....	skills
5 strategy		....	planning
6 challenge	a	....	task
7 administration	an	....	problem
8 profession	a	....	approach

RESPONSIBILITIES   List the verbs in the box in groups of similar meaning to complete the word network. Use the dictionary entries below if necessary.

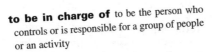

oversee   improve   *monitor*   boost   *sort out*   lead
be in charge of   deal with   *stimulate*   increase
keep an eye on   solve   check   supervise   clear up   manage

keep an eye on
_____
_____   **performance**
_____
_____

solve
_____
_____   **problems**
_____
_____

RESPONSIBILITIES

increase
_____
_____   **profits**
_____
_____

manage
_____
_____
_____   **people**
_____

to be in charge of to be the person who controls or is responsible for a group of people or an activity

to boost to increase something such as production or sales

to check to do something in order to find out whether something that you think is correct, true, or safe, really is correct, true, or safe

to clear up to find the whole explanation for something that is strange and hard to understand

to deal with to take the correct action for a piece of work

to improve to make something better

to lead to be in charge of an important activity or a group of people or an organisation

to monitor to carefully watch and check a situation in order to see how it changes or progresses over a period of time

to oversee to be in charge of a group of workers and check that a piece of work is done satisfactorily

to sort out to deal with problems

to stimulate to make something become stronger

to supervise to be in charge of a group of workers or students and be responsible for making sure they do their work properly

FOCUS ON COMPANIES Read the newspaper report below and then listen to the introduction to a radio business news programme. As you listen, circle any factual mistakes in the written report.

A large number of recent take-overs in Europe, many of them cross-border deals, will keep anti-trust officials at the European (Parliament) busy for months to come.

FERRIER of France, the second-biggest cement maker in the world, has made a hostile £1.7bn ($2.7bn) bid for Britain's REDSTONE, the maker of tiles and aggregates.

The proposed £240m merger between Britain's SUN-UP and THE METRO GROUP in order to create the world's largest drinks maker was confirmed when CORDA, a maker of luxury goods with an interest in Sun-up, made an increased offer of £215m.

GENERAL PROTECTION and UCP are to merge in a £14.1bn deal to create one of Europe's biggest insurance and asset management groups. The combined business will be a strong force in life assurance with a significant presence in the UK, Canada, the US and Eastern Europe.

The new company, to be called CGP, will rank as Britain's second-biggest insurer and Europe's ninth-largest.

The company has announced that its US head-quarters will be in New York, where UCP's head office is already located. However, it did not specify how many of the 2,000 expected job cuts outside the UK would come in North America.

BUSINESS NEWS Part of this newspaper article is difficult to read because of bad printing. Identify the missing words and letters.

TRADITIONAL AND TRENDY

Hewlett Packard is known ▄ as one of the most reputab▄ le suppliers in the electron▄ ics and computer industry.

However, its old-fashion▄ image is now being giv▄ a face-lift as a result ▄ a new advertising campa▄ It has spent $75m on the fi▄ phase of a consumer market▄ drive with a brand-new corpor▄ slogan 'Expanding possibilit▄ The aim is to appeal direct▄ to ordinary people rather t▄ business clients and to transf▄ HP into a global household na▄

Source: The Financial Times, *14 Nov 1997*

Amy MacKenzie has just arrived for a meeting with Jane Mitchell who has not arrived yet. Amy is welcomed by Mary West, Jane Mitchell's personal assistant.

1 Complete the conversation with the phrases in the box.

> *I'll have*   *Can I help you?*   **I'm afraid**   **Do you mind if**
> **Go ahead**   Would you like   Shall I   *sit down*

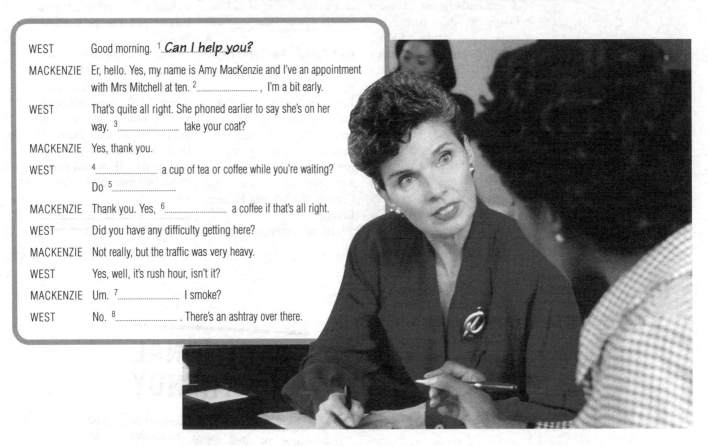

WEST   Good morning. [1] *Can I help you?*

MACKENZIE   Er, hello. Yes, my name is Amy MacKenzie and I've an appointment with Mrs Mitchell at ten. [2] .... , I'm a bit early.

WEST   That's quite all right. She phoned earlier to say she's on her way. [3] .... take your coat?

MACKENZIE   Yes, thank you.

WEST   [4] .... a cup of tea or coffee while you're waiting? Do [5] ....

MACKENZIE   Thank you. Yes, [6] .... a coffee if that's all right.

WEST   Did you have any difficulty getting here?

MACKENZIE   Not really, but the traffic was very heavy.

WEST   Yes, well, it's rush hour, isn't it?

MACKENZIE   Um. [7] .... I smoke?

WEST   No. [8] .... There's an ashtray over there.

2 📼 Listen and check your answers.

Which of these statements are polite and which are impolite in a formal situation? Write *P* or *I* in the boxes.

1 P Have you got a light, please?

2   I want a black coffee.

3   Excuse me, could you tell me where the railway station is?

4   What's the time?

5   I'd like a black coffee.

6   Sit down.

7   Got a light?

8   Where's the railway station?

9   Do take a seat.

10   Excuse me, can you tell me the time?

MEETINGS Read the article below on meetings. Which of these statements would the writer agree with?

	YES	NO
▌ Meetings accelerate the decision-making process.	☐	☐
▌ Meetings produce a synergy effect and generate good ideas.	☐	☐
▌ Committee meetings cannot be avoided.	☐	☐
▌ Dominant individuals may prevent other people from putting forward good ideas.	☐	☐
▌ Better decisions are made by people working by themselves.	☐	☐

According to recent research, managers spend the equivalent of one day a week in internal meetings. Yet meetings are often accused of being inefficient because they discourage original ideas and postpone decision-making. A committee meeting has been described as a group of the unwilling, chosen from the unfit, to do the unnecessary.

So why are there so many meetings? Meetings are said to be a good way to pool resources. Participants may stimulate each other through group discussion – what is known as the synergy effect. According to this view, meetings are an efficient, democratic way to communicate and enable people to make better decisions.

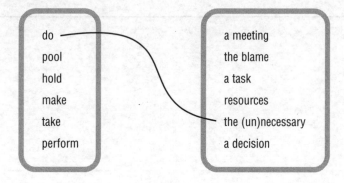

But these arguments are not convincing. Firstly, most meetings are held not to make decisions but to avoid individual responsibility. If a wrong or costly decision is made, fault is spread over all committee members and no one takes the blame.

The second problem is that when making decisions in groups, the presence of some group members with strong personalities can mean that their ideas (right or wrong) are frequently accepted without question.

The third drawback is that when tasks require imagination, groups rather than individuals working alone produce poorer decisions. If an organisation has to make a decision about its declining market share you would expect that a group meeting would solve such a problem better than an individual. However, most research shows that in problem-solving and creative tasks, people perform better on their own.

WORD PARTNERS Match the verbs on the left with the nouns on the right. Check your answers by rereading the article.

do	a meeting
pool	the blame
hold	a task
make	resources
take	the (un)necessary
perform	a decision

JOB DESCRIPTIONS

Complete the sentences with the words and expressions in the box.

salesman   *computer programmer*   **legal department**

chief executive officer   **self-employed**   *personnel manager*

1 I'm a *salesman* and work in the Export Sales department. I have to find new customers for our products.

2 I'm a lawyer and work in the .... I draw up contracts and advise the company on tax legislation.

3 I'm a .... and work in the information technology department. Basically, I design software applications and make sure our website is kept up-to-date.

4 I'm the .... and work in the human resources department. I handle both staff recruitment and training.

5 I'm a management consultant and I'm .... I advise companies on their global strategy and investment policies.

6 I'm the .... and sit on the board of directors. I'm responsible for the company's strategic objectives and translating plans into action.

SCORE: 5

OBLIGATION

Complete the sentences with *mustn't, has to, have to* or *don't have to*.

1 You *mustn't* drink alcohol and drive.

2 Employees .... belong to a union but many choose to do so.

3 You .... be crazy to work in our office but it helps!

4 If you want good service you often .... pay extra.

5 Staff .... take company property home for their personal use without permission.

6 As export sales manager he often .... travel abroad.

■ *For more on* must *and* have to, *go to page 135 of the Course Book.* ■

SCORE: 5

MEETINGS

Read the mini-definitions and write the words.

1 To be present at a meeting. *attend*

2 This should be circulated before the meeting. ....

3 The person who presides over a meeting. ....

4 You write these up after the meeting. ....

5 To suggest a lot of ideas very quickly and at random. ....

6 Are there any other matters to discuss? ....

SCORE: 5

STARTING A MEETING

Complete the extract from a meeting with the expressions in the box.

sort out this mess   **to business**   cancel our regional sales conference
set a time limit   lose $25,000   take the minutes

MIKE   Well, let's get down [1] *to business* . I think our objective is pretty clear. We're here today to
[2] .... We have to decide what we're going to do about the problems with our travel bookings.

PATTI   Sorry, Mike. What problems?

MIKE   It looks like we're going to have to [3] .... and on top of that we're going to [4] ....
or more. Now, I've another meeting at three, so I'd like to [5] .... Is that OK?

BILL   Is anyone writing all this down?

MIKE   Um, no. Harriet, can you [6] .... , please?

SCORE: 5

SOCIAL SKILLS

Complete the questions with the words in the box.

care   excuse me
mind   all right
sorry   please

CONTEXTS	QUESTIONS
On the phone	'Could I speak to Jack Turner, [1] *please?* '
In a hot room	'Do you [2] .... if I open the window?'
At a cocktail party	'Would you [3] .... for an appetiser before we have a drink?'
In a bar	'Do you have a light?' 'No, [4] .... I don't smoke.'
In a railway station	' [5] .... , could you tell me the time?'
At someone's home	'Is it [6] .... if I use your phone?'

SCORE: 5

TOTAL: 25

3 money

MONEY MARKETS Match the words on the left with those on the right.

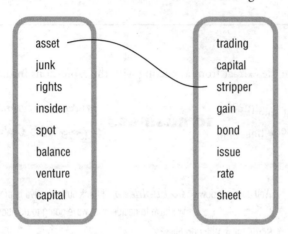

asset	trading
junk	capital
rights	stripper
insider	gain
spot	bond
balance	issue
venture	rate
capital	sheet

FINANCIAL NEWS Listen to the financial news report and fill in the table.

	MOVEMENT (+ OR -)	CLOSING PRICE
TSE-100 Index	+ 10.4	5211.6
Dow Jones Index		
Associated Metals		
RZT Group		
British Fuels		
WTC	+ 3	74
Courtman's		
GLX	+ 11	692
Smith & Parker		
Transpax		
£ Sterling (\$ equivalent)		
International value (% of 1998 level)		

CURRENCIES

1 Circle the fourteen currencies hidden in the puzzle. You can find them by reading horizontally or vertically.

P	Z	R	O	U	B	L	E	T	N
N	L	X	R	W	A	I	I	L	V
C	O	B	I	U	H	A	N	D	L
R	T	P	Y	A	T	L	I	R	A
U	Y	E	A	P	T	Y	U	A	N
Z	R	S	L	D	H	E	R	C	K
E	P	E	S	O	N	N	A	H	E
I	S	T	S	N	C	O	E	M	U
R	Q	A	M	G	J	E	Y	A	R
O	D	R	U	P	E	E	T	T	O

2 Match the currencies with the countries.

Japan	*Yen*	Poland	....
India	....	Vietnam	....
Spain	....	Mexico	....
China	....	Brazil	....
Saudi Arabia	....	Greece	....
Italy/Turkey	....	Russia	....
European Union	....	Thailand	....

GRAPHS Draw a graph to illustrate this short article.

The price of zinc went up slightly by $50 a tonne during the first three months of the year from its turn-of-the-year price of $1,550 a tonne to reach a respectable $1,600. It then rose sharply on 1 April and continued to climb steadily until the end of June when it peaked at a seven-year high of $2,000. Its price on the London Metal Exchange then levelled off for a couple of months before plunging dramatically by 20% in the first week of September. It continued its fall to reach a record low of $1,350 on 3 November. Since then it has picked up gradually and is expected to continue to rise slowly in the coming weeks.

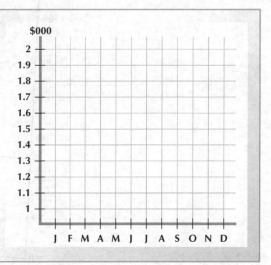

$000
2
1.9
1.8
1.7
1.6
1.5
1.4
1.3
1.2
1.1
1

J F M A M J J A S O N D

CALCULATIONS

Listen to the people making some brief calculations during a meeting. Write down the calculations they make in the spaces provided and complete the graph for calculation 3.

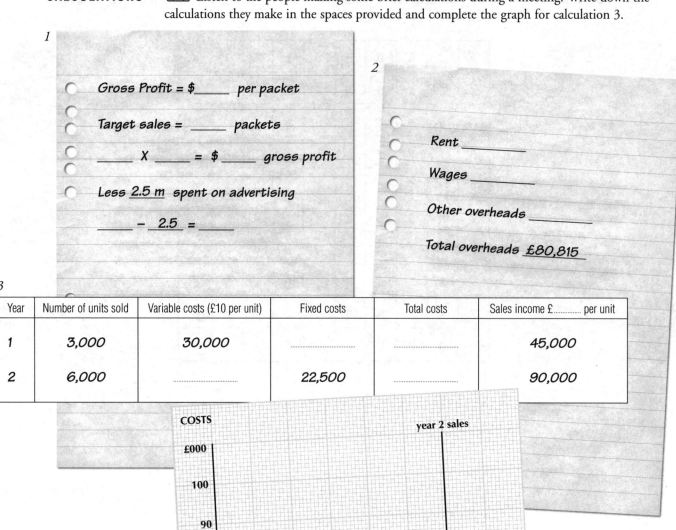

1

Gross Profit = $_____ per packet

Target sales = _____ packets

_____ X _____ = $_____ gross profit

Less <u>2.5 m</u> spent on advertising

_____ – <u>2.5</u> = _____

2

Rent _____

Wages _____

Other overheads _____

Total overheads <u>£80,815</u>

3

Year	Number of units sold	Variable costs (£10 per unit)	Fixed costs	Total costs	Sales income £.......... per unit
1	3,000	30,000	....	....	45,000
2	6,000	....	22,500	....	90,000

COSTS

year 2 sales

£000

100

90

80

70

60

50

40

30   fixed costs

20

10

0   1000 2000 3000 4000 5000 6000

UNIT SALES

ACCOUNTING TERMS   Read these definitions and fill in the balance sheet with the missing terms.

fixed assets
These are items that a firm owns, such as buildings, plant or equipment, and which are necessary for it to do business.

creditors
The amount of money a firm owes to its suppliers of stock.

current assets
These are items owned by a firm whose value changes on a regular basis. They can easily be turned into cash in the normal course of business.

current liabilities
These are amounts owed by a firm. They must be paid on demand or at short notice.

debtors
The amount of money owed to a firm from sales.

de Ryke plc

Balance Sheet

	£m
1 **Fixed assets**	
Plant and machinery	12,925
Premises	5,100
	18,025
2	
Stock	9,125
3	180
Prepayments	365
Bank balance	1,175
	10,845
4	
5	(5,480)
Accrued expenses	(1,725)
Bank loans	(285)
	(7,490)
	21,380

SOCIAL SKILLS   What could you say on each of these occasions? Choose the word or phrase that is best for these situations.

1 You are in an English pub and would like to pay for the drinks at the bar.

2 A colleague tells you she got married exactly ten years ago today.

3 The taxi fare is £17.60 and you give a £20 note.

4 A customer thanks you for giving him a lift to the train station.

5 You didn't understand what someone just said.

6 A visitor asks you if he can use your phone to call head office.

7 A client tells you she won't have time to stay for lunch.

a Go right ahead.
b It's my round.
c Happy anniversary.
d Keep the change.
e That's a pity.
f I beg your pardon.
g Don't mention it.

NUMBER PRONUNCIATION   Choose the correct way of pronouncing the figures in these sentences.

1 The area code is 01865.
   a oh one eight six five
   b one thousand eight hundred and sixty-five
   c one thousand eight hundred sixty-five

2 Their annual turnover is $3.25 bn.
   a three hundred and one four billion dollars
   b three and two five billions dollars
   c three and a quarter billion dollars

3 The train leaves at 14:57.
   a fifty-seven minutes after fourteen
   b three minutes to two
   c fourteen fifty-seven

4 The return fare is £82.
   a pounds eighty-two
   b eighty-two pounds
   c two and eighty pounds

5 The Stock Exchange closed 3.15% down.
   a three point one five per cent
   b three point fifteen per cent
   c three and one five per cent

6 Π (pi) is 3.1428.
   a three dot one four two eight
   b three point fourteen twenty-eight
   c three point one four two eight

BREAKING THE ICE   Match the conversational exchanges.

1 Is this your first time here? **c**

2 How was your flight?

3 I'm from Birmingham.

4 What was the weather like?

5 Do you play football at all?

6 How long are you staying?

7 You must visit the new art gallery while you're here.

8 How was the coffee?

9 What are your children doing these days?

10 How's your wife?

a In England or the United States?
b Is there a special exhibition on?
c No, it's my third visit actually.
d Rained all the time!
e No, but I'm a Juventus supporter.
f Just how I like it.
g I'm going back tomorrow morning, in fact.
h Delayed as usual!
i She's just been promoted.
j Oh, they're both at college now.

TIME IS MONEY   Which of the verbs can be used with both *time* and *money*?

Example: to save time
to save money

to earn   to spare   **to save**   to run out of
to lose   to waste   **to spend**   to raise

OPPOSITES   Match the words with opposite meaning.

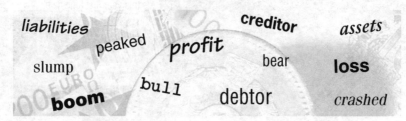

liabilities   peaked   *profit*   **creditor**   *assets*

slump   bear   **loss**

boom   bull   debtor   *crashed*

peaked – crashed ....

....

....

THE LANGUAGE OF GRAPHS   Match the descriptions with the correct graphs.

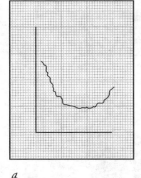   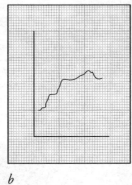   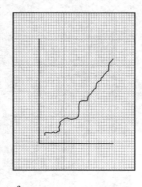   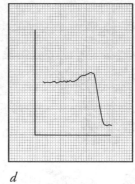   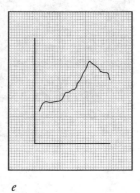

a   *b*   *c*   *d*   *e*

1 Retail demand peaked in December.

2 The Dow Jones has continued to soar.

3 The Nikkei average dipped yesterday in Tokyo.

4 The decrease in the number of union members has hit the bottom and begun to pick up again.

5 The currency market in Thailand collapsed in 1997 and the baht plunged to a record low.

PAST SIMPLE / PAST CONTINUOUS

Complete the article by changing the verbs in brackets into either the past simple or the past continuous.

... and I am sure you will remember that throughout the 1980s and the early 1990s the company's sales [1] *were declining* (decline), we [2] _____ (lose) market share progressively, we [3] _____ (not invest) enough in research and development and we [4] _____ (not train) our key personnel in order for them to use the new technologies.

So, when I [5] _____ (became) Chief Executive Officer in 1997, some tough decisions had to be taken. I [6] _____ (restructure) the management hierarchy, [7] _____ (encourage) early retirement, [8] _____ (cut) costs by 25%, [9] _____ (increase) efficiency by imposing greater flexibility and [10] _____ (close down) three of our factories. The results have been impressive but we [11] _____ (have) to take some tough decisions to get there.

SCORE: 10

FIGURES

Write out the following in figures and symbols.

1 Thirty-five point two billion yen   ¥35.2 bn

2 Three thousand seven hundred and fifty-six pounds _____

3 Seventy-eight point four per cent _____

4 Two thirds _____

5 Twelve point six million Canadian dollars _____

6 One million five hundred and forty-six thousand _____

SCORE: 5

TOTAL: 25

the **market**

LAUNCHING A NEW PRODUCT

1 Read the advertisements below and make sentences matching the features to the benefits.

1

Melbolta

* Our brand-new Melbolta camera bag is not just an attractive case. Behind the highly sophisticated good looks is a bag that will protect your camera for years.

* Melbolta camera bags are made from water-resistant Coralon (found on the inside of car tyres) and nylon which is so strong that it is used in bullet-proof vests for the army.

* Every detail has been professionally engineered to provide years of active protection. All stress points are reinforced and all pockets and walls are fully padded.

5yrs

* The fasteners are designed with a quick-release system so you won't miss that important photo opportunity while trying to get the camera out of the bag.

* We are so sure of Melbolta's reliability that each bag comes with a full five-year guarantee.

FEATURES		BENEFITS
The quick release protection system		the bag won't fall apart.
The five-year guarantee		we believe in our product.
The water-resistant Coralon	mean(s) that	you can get the camera out of the case easily.
The reinforced stress points		the camera inside won't break if you drop the bag.
The protective padding		the camera won't get wet in a thunderstorm.

NEW!!! At last, the performance specifications you've been waiting for! The new POWERPC III has it all. New features include:

- 400MHz for speed of processing
- double the hard disk capacity (8Gb)
- voice navigation
- 128K fax/modem and telecom software
- free Microsoft™ office software plus the other features you've come to expect: anti-glare 21" screen, built-in microphone, ergonomic keyboard and on-site maintenance.

So don't delay: fill in the enclosed pre-paid reply coupon for a visit by one of our representatives or call us on freephone 0800 772227.

And if you wish you can upgrade your existing POWERPC II by purchasing a special plug-in module for a mere £199*.   * subject to availability.

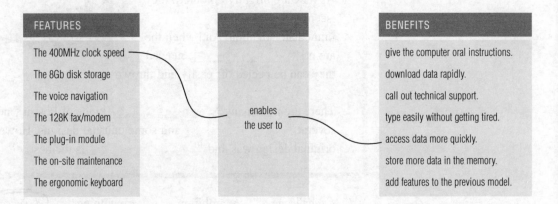

FEATURES		BENEFITS
The 400MHz clock speed		give the computer oral instructions.
The 8Gb disk storage		download data rapidly.
The voice navigation		call out technical support.
The 128K fax/modem	enables the user to	type easily without getting tired.
The plug-in module		access data more quickly.
The on-site maintenance		store more data in the memory.
The ergonomic keyboard		add features to the previous model.

2 Complete the advertisement using the features and benefits below. You will need to join them into a sentence with a verb such as *enable* or *allow*.

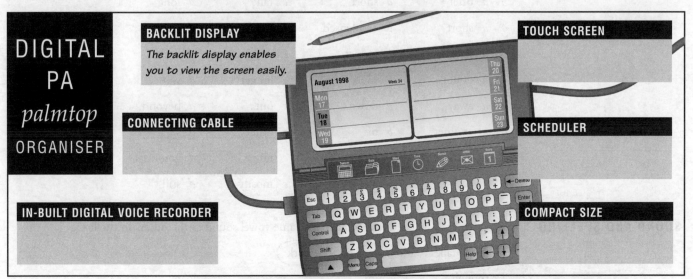

BENEFITS	
record fifteen minutes of messages	move files to and from a desktop PC
launch programs and enter data with a stylus pen	view the screen easily
keep track of your appointments	carry it around in your pocket

THE POST-IT® NOTE   Complete the passage, choosing from the four alternative words for each blank.

Yellow Post-it® notes are now found absolutely everywhere in both offices and the home. So what exactly is the secret of their fantastic commercial ¹ _success_ ?

First, they aren't expensive to ² _____ . Since they are small, the message can't be very ³ _____ , so the writer has to be ⁴ _____ .
As they are brightly-coloured, they seem to ⁵ _____ immediate attention. And when they are no ⁶ _____ needed they can be peeled off easily and thrown ⁷ _____ .

There are now many ⁸ _____ kinds of Post-it® notes: a variety of colours, several ⁹ _____ and some unusual designs. However, most people feel the original design was and ¹⁰ _____ is the best.

CALL JUDITH KNIGHT
URGENTLY
on 01865-512716
RE: CONTRACTS

1	*a* challenge	*b* ambition	*c* winning	*d* success
2	*a* buy	*b* sell	*c* invent	*d* do
3	*a* brief	*b* short	*c* tall	*d* long
4	*a* short	*b* condensed	*c* brief	*d* limited
5	*a* require	*b* attract	*c* ask	*d* wish
6	*a* doubt	*b* more	*c* longer	*d* way
7	*a* away	*b* down	*c* out	*d* beyond
8	*a* another	*b* of	*c* other	*d* such
9	*a* marks	*b* sizes	*c* range	*d* amounts
10	*a* yet	*b* already	*c* mostly	*d* still

SOUND AND SPELLING   Circle the word which does not have the same vowel sound as the others in the list.

Example: t**a**lk   fl**oo**r   l**a**w   (w**or**k)

1	th**ough**	c**ou**nt	gr**ow**	l**oa**n
2	t**ou**gh	en**ou**gh	r**ou**gh	thr**ou**gh
3	c**ou**pon	v**ou**cher	**ou**tlet	backgr**ou**nd
4	**i**mage	w**o**men	s**i**ze	l**i**st
5	dat**a**	fig**u**re	monit**o**r	br**a**nd

ADVERTISING STYLES

Look at the advertisements and choose the adjective that matches the style of each advertisement.

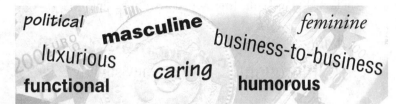

political   masculine   feminine
luxurious   business-to-business
functional   caring   humorous

The following letter announces the launch of a new Metrasure glue gun, the MGG Mark IV. Although this letter states the facts, it is not very convincing. Insert the words in the box where indicated to make the letter sound more appealing.

highly *fully* **convincingly** even enough
thorough only slightly *too good*

Metrasure
136 Farringdon Road London EC1

14 November

Dear Client,

We are pleased to present to you the latest glue gun in our range, the MGG Mark IV.

[1] *Thorough* testing has proved that it is effective at all temperatures and its long-term reliability is [2] .... greater than before. In fact, we are so confident of its performance that it is [3] .... guaranteed for three years.

The MGG Mark IV is [4] .... competitive in price. The cost is, in fact, [5] .... higher than the Mark III.

The MGG Mark IV outperforms its rivals [6] .... on specification and, if that wasn't already good [7] ...., we are offering 5% off list price if you order within the next two weeks. It's [8] .... an opportunity to miss.

Andrew Leaver
Marketing Manager

PS Offer lasts until 28 November

MAKING AN ARRANGEMENT

 Listen and fill in the blanks with the words and expressions the speakers use.

FOURNIER Altavista Enterprises. Can I help you?

GRANT Good morning. My name is John Grant. Can I speak to Monsieur Fournier, please?

FOURNIER Yes, this is Jacques Fournier [1] *speaking*.

GRANT Oh, hello, yes, as I said, my name is John Grant from DDP Services. You may remember we met at the book fair in Stuttgart recently.

FOURNIER Oh yes, that's right. That was in October, [2] _____?

GRANT That's right. Well, [3] _____ our branch in Lille next month and I was wondering if it would be possible for us [4] _____ to meet while I'm in France.

FOURNIER Yes, certainly. When exactly [5] _____?

GRANT From the 4th to the 7th January.

FOURNIER Hold on, I'll just look in my diary. Um. I [6] _____ the 5th January. But [7] _____ the 6th?

GRANT Yes, fine. [8] _____ say at eleven o'clock.

FOURNIER Yes, that suits me fine. And while you're here, [9] _____ have lunch together? There's a very good seafood restaurant near the office.

GRANT Yes, [10] _____. It sounds like a very good idea! There are some very interesting developments I'd like to tell you about.

FOURNIER Right. Well, I [11] _____ you on the 6th.

GRANT Yes. See you then. Goodbye.

FOURNIER Goodbye.

ARRANGEMENTS

Sue Smith wants to make an appointment to see a customer and is asking her secretary to tell her when she is free. Complete the conversation.

SMITH Am I free next Monday morning?

SECRETARY No, you [1] *'re seeing* Mr Webster until midday.

SMITH And in the afternoon?

SECRETARY No, that's not possible either. You [2] _____ the sales conference in London.

SMITH What about Tuesday, then?

SECRETARY Well, in the morning, you [3] _____ the factory in Luton and, in the afternoon, you [4] _____ the new fashion collection but you're OK for Wednesday.

March

9 MONDAY

am ↓ 12 Mr Webster

pm Sales conference (London)

10 TUESDAY

am Visit factory in Luton

pm Presentation of new fashion collection

11 WEDNESDAY

am

pm

ADVERTISING VOCABULARY

Read the clues and write the words in the spaces provided. Use the dictionary definitions if necessary.

Clues

1 We're sending out some promotional literature to try to boost _sales_ .

2 *M* This is a company _____ .

3 British Telecom will _____ the football team if the players all wear BT on their shirts.

4 They've launched an advertising _____ intended to persuade the public that it's an up-market product.

5 Marlboro is a famous _____ of cigarettes.

6 We've decided to _____ the new model at the Paris trade fair in the autumn.

Hidden word

'All the world loves a Coke' is a famous advertising _____ .

1		s	a	l	e	**s**	
2								
3							
4						
5						
6					

SCORE: 5

brand a type of product made by a particular company

campaign a series of actions intended to achieve a particular result

launch to make a new product available for sale for the first time

logo a small design that is the official sign of a company

sales the number of products that a company sells over a period of time

slogan a short clever phrase used in an advertisement, e.g. a dry cleaning company that used the slogan 'We know the meaning of cleaning'.

sponsor to give financial support to a person, organisation or activity

PRESENT PERFECT / PAST SIMPLE

Underline the correct verb form in each sentence.

1   We (<u>discussed</u> / have discussed) it at last week's meeting.
2   He (took up / has taken up) golf six months ago.
3   She (was / has been) with this firm ever since she left college.
4   The accounts (were not / have not been) consolidated yet.
5   Please note that our fax number (changed / has changed).
6   Philip Morris (launched / has launched) the Marlboro brand in 1924.
7   Marlboro (used / has used) cowboys in its advertising since the 1950s.
8   No one told me you were friends. How long (did you know / have you known) each other?
9   He (worked / has worked) for ICI for five years before leaving to set up his own business.
10   So far the group (invested / has invested) only £10 million in new media ventures.
11   Over the last six months the number of our customers using the Internet (grew / has grown) from 25% to 59%.

■ *For more on the past simple and present perfect, go to page 139 of the Course Book.* ■

SCORE: 10

SOCIAL SKILLS

Match the sentences with the headings.

Making an excuse	
Making an invitation	*1*
Making an apology	
Making an offer	
Suggesting a date	

1   Would you like to join me for dinner?
2   How about Monday?
3   I suggest we meet in Brussels on 24 February.
4   Would you like me to make the travel arrangements?
5   I'm afraid I'll be away that week so won't be able to see you.
6   Drop in for a drink when you have time.
7   Shall I send out the invitations?
8   I do apologise for the delay in replying.
9   Dr Hunter requests the pleasure of Mr and Mrs Williams at a cocktail party on 24 May. RSVP.
10   We very much regret any inconvenience caused.
11   I'd really like to help but I've no time.

SCORE: 10

TOTAL: 25

MANAGEMENT
CULTURE

Complete the article using the words in the box. Use a dictionary if necessary.

confident leadership *judgement*
initiative stamina integrity
organisation
accountable communicate

The Qualities of a Successful Manager

What makes a good manager? First of all, the ability to [1] *communicate* , to get your ideas across and to listen to other people. Secondly, a good sense of [2] .... so that working practices are efficient and problems can be anticipated and avoided. Thirdly, managers work long hours and therefore a great deal of [3] .... is required to avoid stress.

A good manager must also be [4] .... in his/her own ability to deal with difficult situations and show qualities of [5] .... so that others will want to follow. Managers have

to take the [6] .... and bring fresh, creative ideas to old problems. But sound [7] .... is necessary when a choice of possible courses of action is difficult or risky.

Once decisions are taken, a manager has to make sure they are implemented and obeyed. For this, he or she must demonstrate [8] .... ; this includes a sense of honesty, trust and loyalty to the organisation and the personnel under his or her control. Managers should also be [9] .... to their own boss and be able to explain the reasons for making any decision.

INTEGRITY COMMUNICATE
ORGANISATION
STAMINA
JUDGEMENT
INITIATIVE
LEADERSHIP
CONFIDENT
ACCOUNTABLE

THEORY X AND
THEORY Y

Make sure you are familiar with the definitions of Theory X and Theory Y (see page 60 of the Course Book). Decide which of these statements belongs to Theory X and which to Theory Y.

	THEORY X	THEORY Y
1 The capacity for imagination and creative work is widely distributed throughout the population.		✔
2 The average person has an inherent dislike of work and will avoid it whenever possible.		
3 The expenditure of physical and mental effort in work is as natural as play and rest.		
4 People will exercise autonomy and self-control in the pursuit of goals to which they are committed.		
5 The majority of people must be forced, directed and even threatened to get them to work towards organisational goals.		
6 The average person is lazy, prefers to avoid responsibility, has little ambition and prefers security above all.		
7 The average person learns not only to accept but also to seek responsibility.		

COPING WITH STRESS

1 Before you read the article, consider the following questions:

	YES	NO
▮ Do you work to live or live to work?	☐	☐
▮ Do you work more than 48 hours a week?	☐	☐
▮ Do you feel exhausted at the end of the day?	☐	☐
▮ Do you spend a lot of time with your family?	☐	☐
▮ Is your quality of life getting better?	☐	☐
▮ Do you think you suffer from stress?	☐	☐

2 Now read the article and compare your lifestyle with the results of the survey described in the article below.

What are we doing to ourselves?
Consider these numbers:

■ 42% of workers feel 'used up' by the end of the day.

■ 69% would like to live a more relaxed life.

■ Parents spend 40% less time with their children than they did 30 years ago.

■ The rise in per capita consumption in the last 20 years is 45%, but the decrease in the quality of life, as measured by the Index of Social Health, is 51%.

■ Only 21% of the young think they have a very good chance of achieving the 'Good Life', compared with 41% 20 years ago.

The numbers are American, but the British already work longer hours, but not necessarily better, than every other country in Europe. An astonishing 36% of non-manual staff work more than 48 hours a week, and they are almost all managers or professionals.

They don't all enjoy it. In a survey by the Institute of Management, 77% considered their hours were stressful, 77% worried about the effect on their family and 74% about their relationship with their partner. Stress costs Britain 40 million working days a year and £7 billion in health care.

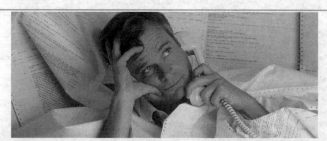

So why do we do it? Could it be that some people actually prefer their work to the other parts of their lives? Have we changed the comfort of the lifetime job for the philosophy of a corporate marketplace in which you are only as good as your last project or report, when the best will thrive and the less good will be ejected?

If this is what is happening, the consequences are worrying. A competitive philosophy within the firm will encourage people to look first to their own interests, and only secondly to the interests of the firm they work for. The short term will dominate their thinking while the competition for personal recognition will make cooperation and teamwork even more difficult than it already is, across functions, countries and language.

At the altar of the machine by Charles Handy, The Observer, *31 August 1997*

---

3 Decide if these statements are true or false.

	T	F
1 According to the survey, British managers have improved productivity by working long hours.	☐	☐
2 The writer thinks that current working practices are not good for the economy.	☐	☐

4 What two predictions for the future of working practices does the writer make?

....

....

5 Do you agree with him?

1 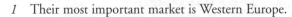 Listen to a radio interview with Dr Young about his organisation Oxford Business Briefs, which provides daily information bulletins to clients in international business. Are these statements true or false? Correct the false statements.

T   F

1 Their most important market is Western Europe.

2 The Business Briefs provide more analysis than newspaper and magazine reports.

3 Dr Young knows well in advance what subjects customers will find interesting.

4 The Washington official thought that the brief he read had been useful.

2 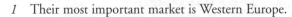 Listen again and answer these questions.

1 What are Oxford Business Briefs?

....

2 Who produces them?

....

3 Who are their major clients?

....

4 What is the format for each brief?

....

5 How useful does Scott Walker find them?

....

WELCOMING A VISITOR  Mario Pelleschi has just arrived for his appointment with Linda Roberts. Listen and fill in the blanks.

ROBERTS   Hello. You must be Mario Pelleschi. My name is Linda Roberts. I've been expecting you.

PELLESCHI   Hello. Very pleased to meet you.

ROBERTS   [1] *Did* you *have* a good flight?

PELLESCHI   Yes, although we were late taking off.

ROBERTS   And [2] .... exactly .... you ....?

PELLESCHI   Oh, it's a small hotel called the Queen Victoria in Lombard Street.

ROBERTS   The Queen Victoria? [3] .... away .... from here?

PELLESCHI   Not far, about a kilometre, that's all.

ROBERTS   [4] .... you .... here?

PELLESCHI   No, no, I took a taxi.

ROBERTS   [5] .... you .... a seat?

PELLESCHI   Thank you.

ROBERTS   [6] .... are you staying in London?

PELLESCHI   Just a couple of days. Then I'm flying to Dublin. [7] .... you .... been there?

ROBERTS   No, never. [8] .... it .... at this time of year?

PELLESCHI   Cold and wet!

ROBERTS   I'm not surprised! OK. Well, let's get down to business, shall we?

CONVERSATIONS   Match the questions with an appropriate reply.

1 Do you know each other?

2 How are things?

3 I have an appointment with Mr Lindberg.

4 Did you have any problems finding us?

5 Your appointment is for 11:30, isn't it?

a Yes, that's right.

b No, it was easy getting here.

c Fine, thanks.

d I'll see if he's in his office.

e We've never met actually.

1 These are some of the replies that were given during a job interview. Write the questions. (Pay attention to the underlined words.)

Example:
When did you leave business school?
I left business school <u>in 1995</u>.

1

....
I decided to leave TLM because <u>I wasn't given enough responsibility</u>.

2

....
I've been in my present position <u>since 1997</u>.

3

....
At the moment I earn <u>£35,000 a year</u>.

4

....
It took me <u>about forty-five minutes</u> to drive here from home.

5

....
We've short-listed <u>five candidates</u>.

6

....
We became a public limited company <u>six years ago</u>.

7

....
We employ <u>over six hundred people</u>.

8

....
Our turnover has increased <u>by 15%</u>.

9

....
We have a planning meeting <u>once a month</u>.

10

....
Staff development is <u>Mr Carter's</u> responsibility.

2 🔲 Listen and check your questions.

DEVELOPING A CONVERSATION

When we are taking part in a conversation we need to react to what the other person is saying. This helps to show that we are interested and want to keep the conversation going.

Listen and write down what Tony says in reaction to what Richard says.

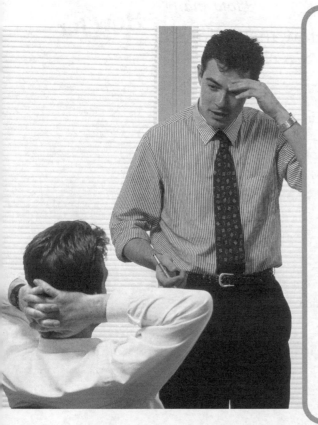

RICHARD	Did I tell you that I had an interview for that job that was advertised in *The Times*?
TONY	1 ....
RICHARD	Well, I got the job.
TONY	2 ....
RICHARD	But I didn't take it.
TONY	3 ....
RICHARD	A number of things really. The job was in central London and you know what it's like coming in on the train every day.
TONY	4 ....
RICHARD	And the salary they were offering wasn't fantastic, less than what I'm on now.
TONY	5 ....
RICHARD	On the other hand, the job itself was interesting, with the possibility of lots of travel in the Far East.
TONY	6 ....
RICHARD	But then again I didn't really want to leave Carol on her own with the children and she's in the middle of a reorganisation at work.
TONY	7 .... Still, it's a pity about the salary because ...

REPHRASING

1 Another way of showing interest is by restating something in a slightly different way. Read the following conversation and try to predict what B says in each case.

Example:
A I've heard that they're doing well.   B Yes, they're very successful.

A I hear she's a very organised person.

B Yes, she's extremely ¹ ....

A The advertising campaign has had a great impact.

B Yes, it's been very ² ....

A He's spent his entire career with General Motors.

B Yes, he's the perfect example of a ³ ....

A Companies have to think international if they're going to survive.

B Yes, it's all part of the ⁴ .... of the economy.

A The price of international phone calls has gone down by at least 20%.

B Yes, they've ⁵ ....

A They manage to keep their prices below those of their rivals.

B Yes, they're very ⁶ ....

A The secret of their success lies in mass production.

B Yes, they benefit from ⁷ ....

A The new technology is a great leap forward.

B Yes, it's a major ⁸ ....

A They've re-engineered the whole operation.

B Yes, there's been a great ⁹ ....

A Did you know Jane has tendered her resignation?

B Yes, she ¹⁰ .... yesterday.

2 Listen and check.

QUESTIONS WITH HOW

Write the question for each answer.

How   How often   *How many*

How much   How many times   **How far**

1   <u>*How do you usually come to work?*</u>

I usually come to work by public transport.

2   ....

They employ over 2,000 people.

3   ....

I spoke to him on five separate occasions.

4   ....

I expect to earn at least £50,000 a year.

5   ....

The plant is about five miles from the station.

6   ....

We have a planning meeting every fortnight.

SCORE: 5

FUTURE

Complete the article with *will* or *won't*.

The world is getting smaller and therefore companies [1] <u>*will*</u> have to become more international in their outlook as they [2] .... be able to rely exclusively on their domestic markets. New technologies [3] .... make global communications even easier so managers [4] .... be forced to travel long distances any longer and instead [5] .... increasingly speak to their counterparts abroad using video telephony or video-conferencing. In addition, the Internet [6] .... stimulate electronic commerce and the general public [7] .... get used to ordering and purchasing goods directly from a computer screen.

However, there is a danger that the gap between rich and poor nations [8] .... increase if these technologies are too expensive for developing countries. But it is also very likely that European nations [9] .... be able to compete for much longer with low-cost countries such as India or China. Emerging nations [10] .... certainly want a larger slice of the world's cake and [11] .... let today's richest nations keep an unfair share of the world's economic resources.

■ *For more on the future forms, go to page 133 of the Course Book.* ■

SCORE: 10

A JOB ADVERT   Complete the job advertisement with the words in the box.

benefits   looking for   leading

run

track record   performance-related

Marketing Manager: *Bilbao*

Syscom, a leading company in the field of netware and electronic commerce, is
[1] _looking for_ a marketing manager to [2] .... its office in northern
Spain. Based in Bilbao, the person appointed will work closely with local personnel
and play a [3] .... role in the newly-created marketing function with
specific responsibility for advertising and public relations throughout the region.

He/She will be a graduate with a working knowledge of English and Spanish. He/She
must have a [4] .... in a marketing environment and have excellent
communication and interpersonal skills.

In addition to the [5] .... salary, we provide an attractive [6] ....
package including accommodation and company car.

Please send your full c.v. to Rebecca Byrne.

SCORE: 5

WORD PARTNERS   Match the words on the left with those on the right.

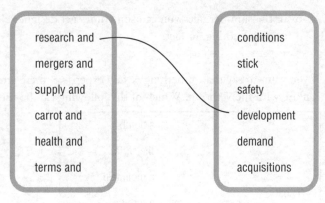

research and	conditions
mergers and	stick
supply and	safety
carrot and	development
health and	demand
terms and	acquisitions

SCORE: 5

TOTAL: 25

6 the **customer**

PRICES

1 The following dictionary entries all refer to prices. List them on a scale from high (1) to low (6).

> ☐ **giveaway** if a shop is selling goods at rock bottom or giveaway prices, it is selling them extremely cheaply
>
> ☐ **costly** too expensive and wasting a lot of money
>
> **1** **rip-off** an informal expression meaning to cheat someone by charging them much more than the agreed or usual price for something
>
> ☐ **reasonable** reasonable prices are not too high and you think they are fair
>
> ☐ **cheaply** costing very little money, but not always of the best quality
>
> ☐ **free** without payment

2 Complete the sentences with the words.

1 You don't have to pay to park at the supermarket, it's *free* .

2 $12 for a glass of cola – what a .... !

3 Buying all that incompatible software was a .... mistake.

4 They make good products at .... prices that the average consumer can afford.

5 You can pick up several things quite .... at our local market.

6 In the summer sales you can sometimes get designer clothes at .... prices – for next to nothing, in fact.

IDIOMS

If you want to say that something is very expensive, there are a number of expressions that you can use with the verb *cost*. Which of the following can be used?

	a bomb.
	the earth.
	a mountain.
It cost	a fortune.
	an elephant.
	an arm and a leg.
	a packet.

TIMING A SALE Read the following passage from a sales training manual and decide which of the sentence endings fit into the gaps (1–7).

Before rushing in to make a sale, it is important to think about the time scale involved. If your customer doesn't know you or your company, ... [1]. But if the buyer is not very impressed by your initial presentation, ... [2]. Also, if you know the buyer's decision-making process will take several months, ... [3].

Timing a sale is crucial. Suppose you receive a call from a company that wants you to supply a product or service designed to meet a very specific set of needs. And suppose that you already have something that corresponds exactly to what this company is looking for.

But even if you have what this customer wants, it may be better not to say so immediately. If you are going to be seen as doing something special to satisfy individual needs, ... [4]. If you call back the next day, ... [5]. But if you give a precise time for a return call ... [6].

So take a moment to consider whether the situation demands a certain timing strategy or if you can use timing to your advantage. If it doesn't, and if you can't, ... [7].

	you can always call back straightaway.
	you need time to pass between the customer's request and your solution.
	the client will wait and be pleased to hear your proposals.
	try a different approach before presenting it again.
	the customer will wonder how you managed to provide an individualised response so quickly.
1	a sale will take longer to secure than if he/she does.
	don't try to force a commitment out of him/her after several weeks.

3

WORD PARTNERS Which words in the box can combine with each of the words listed in each group?

demand *price* **decision** *market*

1 budget
  cost
  cut   ....
  retail
  unit

2 final
  right
  snap   ....
  unanimous
  wise

3 boost
  create
  meet   ....
  satisfy
  strengthen

4 black
  competitive
  domestic   ....
  export
  target

THE ART OF PERSUASION

1 Before you read the article think about the following questions:

▌ Have you ever bought something you didn't intend to and regretted it afterwards?

▌ What qualities do you think a good salesperson should have?

2 Read the article. Which of these statements is supported by it?

	YES	NO
▌ It's best to offer the customer a choice.		
▌ You can make anyone buy anything.		
▌ A good salesperson finds out what the customer wants to buy.		
▌ To make a sale you need to get the customer on your side.		
▌ A salesperson should be a good psychologist.		
▌ It's a good idea in selling to let the customer think about it and come back later.		

'Insurance is a terrible investment,' the salesman told his prospect. The customer agreed, but was surprised to hear such a comment from a man he had thought was trying to sell him a policy.

'But you have to admit it offers protection in an emergency,' the salesman continued. Again the customer agreed. He did not realise it, but the sale was as good as made.

As the salesman continued to discuss the policy, he returned to his original statement each time he felt a resistance from the client. And with the customer again in agreement that 'Insurance is a terrible investment' the salesman continued to bring him along one step at a time until the policy was signed.

This approach is typical and illustrates the idea that the most effective way to change a person is to get their agreement. Then they will follow wherever you want them to go.

The skilled salesperson is also able to elicit personal information to use later and can 'read' a prospective customer through the way he dresses and talks and his body language. Trust and rapport is built up through the use of vague, unspecific conversation which enables the customer to make his own interpretation of what the sales person is saying. There is nothing easier than selling someone his or her 'own' idea.

So a car salesperson might say 'I'd like to help you get the model you're interested in.' Such a remark cannot be challenged and once agreement has been established the salesperson watches out for the

prospect's values and uses that to create confidence and a feel-good factor. If he/she notices that petrol consumption and safety are important to the client he/she concentrates on those areas.

The salesperson may even insert commands into the conversation. The salesperson may say something like 'The smart investor knows how to make a quick decision, Mr Smith.' Perhaps he/she will repeat that several times and then say quickly: 'The smart investor knows how to, Mr Smith make a quick decision.'

Not everyone thinks selling takes place in this way. Robert Burke, an industrial psychologist, has written 'If a person really does not want to buy, then no sales technique or hypnotic suggestion will make him do so.' This is some comfort certainly, but the next time you're thinking of buying a new car, watch out for the smartly-dressed salesperson with a watch and chain and a strange look in his/her eye.

▌ **GLOSSARY** ▌

policy	*insurance contract*
elicit	*to get a response*
trust	*confidence*

BARGAINING　　[cassette] Listen to the conversation about the purchase of some machinery and note each person's negotiating position.

	PROPOSAL			COUNTER PROPOSAL
	pay for delivery			

WORD PARTNERS　　Which of the words in the box come before the word *sales* and which come after?

car　forecast

technique

revenue　　*figures*

export

retail　　home

BEFORE	AFTER
export sales	

FOOD AND DRINK　　Organise the vocabulary into the groups.

Menu	Spices	Vegetables	Meat	Fruit
starters				
main course				
dessert				

Seafood	Types of drink	Ways of cooking	Taste	Cutlery

pork　curry　cinnamon　spoon　　*ginger*　bake

cherry　　fork　main course　　fry　sour

cauliflower　*spicy*　*liver*　spinach　prawn

pear　starters　still　roast　dry　cabbage

shrimp　dessert　lobster　knife　apricot　bitter　lamb

sparkling

SPONSORSHIP

You are the Marketing Manager of Cocelli, a textiles firm which designs and manufactures sportswear, which is then sold through a number of franchised outlets at home and abroad.

You are planning to invest approximately £500,000 in sponsorship in order to improve your firm's image and reputation.

1 Read through the following information files and make notes for each proposal under the following headings:

▪ Description   ▪ Cost   ▪ Advantages to the company   ▪ Disadvantages to the company

Cocelli

Susan Forster

Many sport writers are predicting that 15-year-old Susan Forster will be Britain's first great tennis champion and will come to dominate the world tennis circuit in the same way as Martina Navratilova and Chris Evert did in their time.

She recently won the Italian Open, beating her opponent 6-0, 6-0. But she needs money (£450,000) to help her parents pay for travel expenses, coaching and a private tennis court to practise on.

If we were to sponsor her, she would wear a T-shirt, sweater and skirt made by Cocelli and our name and logo would figure prominently on close-up television shots.

Notes:

_____

_____

_____

_____

Cocelli

Rodney Hull

The famous skipper Rodney Hull is looking for sponsors to finance his participation in the Round the World catamaran race to be held next year. Five years ago, Hull won the San Francisco solo competition in record time. He has asked for £650,000.

The race is given television coverage in a number of countries. Last year, Hull was forced to quit when he was in the lead because of a broken mast. However, this was not a total disaster because as Hull says, 'It is better to be forced to abandon the race when the cameras are on you, rather than make no impact at all'.

If we were to sponsor him, the firm's name and logo would be prominently displayed on his clothing and catamaran. He would also make sure he mentioned our name to the press as often as possible, together with the other firms helping him to purchase his catamaran.

Notes:

_____

_____

_____

Cocelli

Winstanley United Football Supporters' Club

Winstanley United football supporters' club is looking for a sponsor to finance the purchase of four coaches which would be used to transport supporters to matches in Britain and abroad. These coaches would be suitably decorated and our name and logo would be painted in bright colours on the sides of the bus and, in their view, be a 'great travelling advertisement'. In addition, our name would be associated with the name of a club which has consistently been successful in national and international competitions.

Notes:

_____

_____

_____

_____

_____

2 Draft a memo to the Marketing Director, putting forward your recommendation and giving your reasons for it.

Cocelli

Memo

I have received three requests for sponsorship. After studying them carefully and making additional enquiries I feel that we should use the £500,000 earmarked for sponsorship on …

CHECK YOUR PERFORMANCE

VOCABULARY   Write the verbs that correspond to the nouns.

1 agreement   *agree*

2 concession   _____

3 loan   _____

4 negotiation   _____

5 offer   _____

6 refusal   _____

SCORE: 5

PAYMENT   Match the two halves of the sentences.

1 You have to pay   a the money I borrowed.

2 I usually pay by   b the cashier.

3 I'll pay for   c the meal.

4 I'm trying hard to pay off   d $68.45.

5 I must remember to pay back e bank transfer.

6 The bill comes to   f a huge bank loan.

SCORE: 5

CONDITIONALS   Match the two halves of the sentences.

1 So we've agreed on the price.
  Now, if you pay cash,

2 It's a fact of life. If you don't advertise,

3 It's well-known that if you give your
  client too much time to think,

4 According to the public relations people,
  if you sponsored a charity,

5 Times are hard. If it saved my job,

6 I know they can be a nuisance but if
  you didn't have a mobile phone,

a no one will recognise the name
  of your products.

b you'll lose the sale.

c I'll give you a 5% discount.

d you wouldn't be able to contact
  head office so easily.

e you'd improve your reputation.

f I'd take a cut in salary.

SCORE: 5

MORE CONDITIONALS Put the verbs in brackets into the correct forms.

1 If share prices continue to fall, we __'ll lose__ (lose) a lot of money.

2 If we __paid__ (pay) the transport costs, would you reduce the unit price?

3 If the men call off the strike, we _____ (negotiate).

4 If our competitor _____ (go) bankrupt, we'll increase our market share.

5 If we _____ (change) the packaging, we'd sell more.

6 If we asked for easy credit terms, they _____ (not agree).

7 If a firm _____ (offer) me a bribe to get an important contract, I'd ask 'How much?'

■ *For more on the conditionals, go to page 130 of the Course Book.* ■

SCORE: 5

FOOD AND DRINK Match the two parts of the conversational exchanges.

1 How do you take your coffee?	a No, thanks. I'm driving.
2 It's my round.	b It's very spicy.
3 Sorry, sir. The fish is off.	c White, no sugar. Thanks.
4 Another whisky?	d Well-done, please.
5 How would you like it?	e No, this one is on me.
6 What does it taste like?	f In that case, I'll have the steak.

SCORE: 5

TOTAL: 25

7 production

PROJECT TEAMWORK **1** Complete this paragraph with the words in the box. Use a dictionary if necessary.

set up   *smoothes*   ensure   *training*
involves   **stage**   brief   *standard*

THE CREATION *of a new product and its manufacturing processes* [1] *involves* *research into marketing, investment, production techniques and supplier relations as well as technical and sales staff* [2] _____ . *The aim is to guarantee a high* [3] _____ *of quality and to* [4] _____ *a competitive price tag while at the same time fully respecting the initial* [5] _____ . *For optimal results, manufacturers* [6] _____ *a team of experts who work under the Project Director and follow the new project all the way through to production. This system is not only more economical, it also* [7] _____ *the transition from the design* [8] _____ *to production and delivery to the point of sale.*

1 _____

Even though their own particular speciality might involve the design, production or sale of the new car, the members of the Project Team have a clear overall picture of the project and are in a better position to identify and explain to their colleagues a potential problem they foresee arising at a later date. The Project Team is formed around a stable core of staff who, in addition to pooling their respective skills, are able to communicate with, motivate and train others.

2 _____

Previously, when a decision had been taken to proceed with a new model, the relevant departments of the company intervened one after the other. Each department would simply pass the project on. This sequential, step-by-step approach assumed that if the input from each successive department was of the best quality, then the final product would be too. Unfortunately, the system was extremely long and the end result did not always match expectations.

2 A publishing company is preparing a book on car production. Match the headings with the text.

	EVEN SHORTER LEAD TIMES
	MATRIX ORGANISATION
1	THE PROJECT TEAM: A BROAD OVERVIEW
	THE FORMER METHOD: A SEQUENTIAL PROCESS
	THE SPECIALISTS TAKE OVER
	THE CHAIN OF COMMAND

3

The work of the Project Team involves even the tiniest detail of the new car. It therefore tends to be sub-divided into specialist functional groups. Each is responsible for its own particular field such as body sides, dashboards, engines, etc. In many cases, in-house specialists work hand in hand with outside suppliers and each 'sub-group' is bound by a Quality/Cost/Delivery contract with the Project Director.

4

The Project Team works under the overall supervision of the Project Director who reports directly to senior management. The Design, Product and Process Engineering, Manufacturing, Financial and Administrative Departments are obliged to release any of their specialist staff or information the Project Director requests.

5

Project management has already resulted in considerable gains in the time required to develop a new model, which today is approximately three years.

6

The traditional vertical organisation of companies has today been complemented by a number of cross-functional structures, such as the Project Team, which involve a broad range of specialists working together to solve a given problem. This is known as the 'matrix' structure.

THE LEAN ENTERPRISE

1 Read the passage below from a seminar on Total Quality Management. Underline the disdavantages of mass production. Identify the four things that have to be done to make production lean.

1 ....

■ GLOSSARY ■

attain *reach*
benchmarking *measuring and comparing*

2 ....

3 ....

4 ....

TOTAL QUALITY MANAGEMENT

We're worried about quality certainly because of a basic frustration with the era of mass production that we have been living through for the last 40 or 50 years.

And when I talk about mass production, I am not simply talking about how Henry Ford organised his factories, I'm talking about a complete way of looking at the world, at how we live, what we make and how we think of our customers. Mass production was something we actually didn't like in Europe. It could never offer rewarding jobs to its employees and I think it's becoming evident that it could not also offer rewarding jobs to engineers either.

And it has become clear in recent years that mass production can also not attain high levels of quality. Perhaps the solution is to become a lean enterprise.

To do this you need to do four things. You need to make the crisis visible by benchmarking performance. You need to make a very clear commitment at the top to change your objectives and, in particular, to delegate. The enterprise should be organised around the process flows, not around the traditional functions. And, finally, you need to create lots of examples of lean best practice: 'seeing is believing' is terribly powerful at changing attitudes.

2 🔲 Listen to the presentation.

WORD BUILDING Use the word in capitals to make another word that will fit into the sentences.

PRODUCT

1 We don't expect the prototype to go into __*production*__ before next year.

2 They can't give the employees a pay raise without an increase in ....

3 The meeting was very .... and we got a lot of things done.

COMMIT

4 Our firm is .... to the highest standards of quality.

5 You can't impose quality policies; you need the .... of the work force.

OPERATE

6 She has a job as a machine .... on the production line.

7 Repairs have begun and we expect the factory to be fully .... soon.

A COMPANY REPORT

1 Read this extract from a supermarket chain's annual report. Match the causes and effects.

SuperSave

We achieved strong sales growth, with stores increasing their sales by 8.9% on account of the boom in consumer spending. However, the market continues to be highly competitive. Our ongoing commitment to offering customers excellent value for money has meant we have reduced selling prices on many products. As a result of improvements in our sales mix, better buying and more efficient sourcing, we have been able to limit the impact of lower prices on gross margins, which fell by only 0.2%.

We have continued our drive to improve productivity. This has helped to finance the significant improvements to checkout service and more labour-intensive departments such as pharmacies. Consequently, wages as a percentage of sales reduced by 0.4% to 9.3% and other operating costs went down by 0.5%.

We continue to invest in supporting infrastructure. We have opened a new automatic warehouse which has led to reduced stock levels. We have also continued with the streamlining of our supply system which has meant that more products are available to customers and supply costs are lower than previously.

Our capital expenditure for the year was £649m which is higher than we anticipated three years ago. However, this is partly due to our ability to negotiate planning permission for new sites and partly to investment in extensions to existing stores.

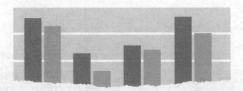

CAUSE	EFFECT
a highly competitive market	higher capital expenditure than previously
improved productivity	a very small reduction in gross margins
investment in new stores and extensions	reduced price tags
boom in consumer spending	sales growth of 8.9%
better supply system	fewer items in stock
better buying and more efficient sourcing	reduced wages and lower overheads
an automatic warehouse	more products on the shelves

2 Underline the words in the text that signal a cause and effect.

Example: on account of

VERBS OF RESULT

1 Look at the way these words are used.

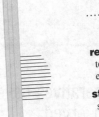

result in finally cause a particular situation to exist, at the end of a process or series of events

stem from to happen or exist as a result of something

2 Choose from the verbs above to complete these sentences. Change the form of the verb when necessary.

1 Advertising during the Christmas trading period usually _____ increased sales.

2 The dispute _____ a disagreement over the interpretation of the contract.

3 The fire in the warehouse has _____ millions of pounds of damage.

1 Read the informal note that John Elliott sent to his Production Director, Martin Gilmour.

> Martin,
>
> Bob Skinner recently told me that some of the men are not following safety procedures. He's seen operatives not wearing hard hats or protective gloves, and doing silly things just to keep the line moving. If we don't do something about it very soon, someone is bound to get hurt.
>
> John

2 Now rewrite the letter as a formal memo using the phrases below.

MEMO

To: Martin Gilmour
From: John Elliott
Date: 23 March

It has come to my attention that ...

operatives have been observed

are failing to comply with safety procedures

and taking dangerous risks

a number of employees

it has come to my attention that

unless preventive measures are taken swiftly

a serious injury will be inevitable

in order to maintain the rate of production

without protective clothing

Culture and lunch

1 When hosting foreign guests, would you take them to restaurants specialising in their national food? Why/Why not?

2 Would you entertain a business visitor in your own home? Why/Why not?

3 What kinds of food would you not offer to
a Muslims?
b Hindus?
c Orthodox Jews?

4 In the United States, the entrée is
a the starter.   **b** the main dish.   **c** the dessert.

5 In Oriental cultures, placing chopsticks parallel across your bowl or plate means
a you would like some more.
b you have had enough.
c you need something to drink.

**TOPICS OF
CONVERSATION**

Listen to the people talking to each other and identify the subjects of their conversations.

films   **food**   **family**   tourist attractions
mutual friends   economics   *politics*   sport

Conversation 1 ....

Conversation 2 ....

Conversation 3 ....

Conversation 4 ....

Conversation 5 ....

CHECK YOUR PERFORMANCE

PRODUCING TO ORDER Complete the text with the words in the box.

mass-produced 'just-in-time' **demand** logistics specifications
delivery

HIGHLY STANDARDISED cars like the Ford Model T were [1] *mass-produced* , then stock-piled until they were sold. However, today's motorists not only want a car which closely matches their personal needs, they also want to take [2] _____ of it as quickly as possible. To meet this [3] _____ in today's highly competitive marketplace, manufacturers are bringing out an increasing number of versions of a given model. To avoid an unacceptable increase in inventory and costs, companies now produce cars only when a confirmed order is placed. This [4] _____ principle involves complicated [5] _____ in which both production and information are closely linked. When a contract has been signed, the precise [6] _____ for the car the customer has ordered are communicated to a central database and consulted by the sales and production staff in order to plan production schedules.

SCORE: **5**

COMPOUND NOUNS Match the words on the left with those on the right to make five compound nouns.

mass	floor
quality	leader
team	station
assembly	production
work	control
shop	line

SCORE: **5**

CAUSES AND EFFECTS Look at the dictionary entries and complete the sentences with *as a result of* and *led to*.

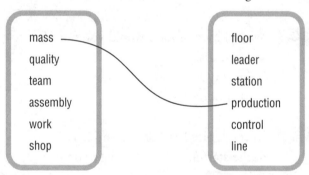

as a result of because of something that has happened

led to made something happen

1 The oil crisis of the 1970s *led to* economies in energy consumption in Europe.

2 The production line was shut down for two hours _____ damaged machinery.

3 The assassination of the president _____ serious political instability in the country.

4 Ignoring safety procedures _____ a tragic accident.

5 He turned a £10,000 investment into more than £300 million _____ investing at the time of maximum pessimism.

6 Profits have decreased _____ a decline in sales.

SCORE: **5**

DESCRIBING A PROCESS

Complete the flow chart using either the active or passive form of the verb in brackets as appropriate.

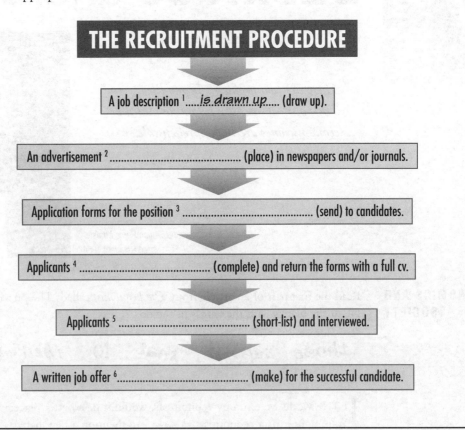

THE RECRUITMENT PROCEDURE

A job description [1] ...*is drawn up*... (draw up).

An advertisement [2] .... (place) in newspapers and/or journals.

Application forms for the position [3] .... (send) to candidates.

Applicants [4] .... (complete) and return the forms with a full cv.

Applicants [5] .... (short-list) and interviewed.

A written job offer [6] .... (make) for the successful candidate.

SCORE: 5

PROOF READING

Find the errors in the use of active and passive verb forms. Underline them and correct them.

THE MEETING <u>was discussed</u> the four tenders for the proposed new installation. The first of these feel to be too expensive and the second and the third were rejected because it considered they did not comply with our safety standards. The installation which choose is within our budget and meets our technical specifications. It agreed therefore that work on the new installation would begin before the end of the year. The minutes of the meeting distributed to the share holders. ■

1 ....*discussed*............................   4 ....

2 ....   5 ....

3 ....   6 ....

■ *For more on the passive, go to page 137 of the Course Book.* ■

SCORE: 5

TOTAL: 25

8 business and society

> *There are two problems in my life. The political ones are insoluble and the economic ones are incomprehensible.*

Sir Alec Douglas-Home, British Prime Minister,
speech January 1964

ECONOMICS AND SOCIETY

Read the first part of an article from *The Economist* called 'The puzzling failure of economics'. Fill in the blanks with the words in the box.

those *not* **if** **that** to *their* **so** such

IF THE world were run by economists, would it be a better place? You might expect economists, [1] *not* to mention a newspaper called *The Economist*, to think [2] _____ . After all, many of the policies [3] _____ people fight over have economics at [4] _____ core – jobs, wages, investment, growth. Economists, professional or otherwise, are forever criticising [5] _____ who do run the world for making [6] _____ a mess of it, and are keen to change the way people think so that things will run more [7] _____ their liking. As one Nobel Laureate put it, 'I don't care who writes a nation's laws ... [8] _____ I can write its economics textbooks.'

The Economist, *August 23 1997*

COLLOCATIONS

Complete the expressions with the words in the box.

means *balance* **standard** **law** round *product*

1 the __law__ of supply and demand

2 a country's _____ of payments

3 a country's Gross National _____

4 the _____ of production

5 the latest _____ of negotiations

6 the _____ of living

DEDUCTIONS   Read the five profiles below and comment on each one using *can't be* and *must be*.

With a succession of hits such as *Who's that Girl?* and *Like a Virgin*, Mick Jagger has proved that he is more than just an ordinary pop star. He has had considerable success in publishing, film and video (*In Bed With Mick Jagger* was a huge international success) while his business skills have enabled him to become one of the highest-paid singers in the music industry.

Example:

    ...This can't be about Mick Jagger. It must be about Madonna...

Anita Roddick was born in 1950, and by 1971 had established Virgin mail order and opened the first Virgin record store in Oxford Street. In 1972 she signed the first artist to the Virgin label, Mike Oldfield, whose *Tubular Bells* sold over five million copies. An unconventional entrepreneur, she has diversified into Virgin Coke, Virgin Airlines, Virgin Games and Virgin Cargo and has signed a 15-year franchise to run a railway network in Britain.

1 ....

Ted Turner started in the computer industry while at school and was a billionaire by the age of 31. A combination of technical brilliance and tough business tactics quickly made him the most powerful man in Silicon Valley. However, he wanted his company Microsoft to be more than just a software house and in recent years it has diversified into many new fields.

2 ....

Richard Branson launched the TV news network CNN in 1980. A lot of its success has been due to Branson's bold risk taking and inspirational management. He once told his employees, 'We're on a pirate ship at sea. We're going to go out and raid all the other ships on the ocean.'

3 ....

Bill Gates was one of the founders of the Sony corporation, and its CEO for many years. He trained as an engineer and throughout his career made sure that Sony was at the leading edge of technology. He also had a brilliant understanding of the market and was responsible for the success of the Sony Walkman®.

4 ....

Since it started in 1976, Akio Morita's Body Shop has grown from a tiny business to become a multinational cosmetics company. The Body Shop never uses direct advertising but gets publicity through campaigns on international social and environmental issues.

5 ....

MORE DEDUCTIONS

1 Complete the conversations using the verb in brackets and *must have* or *can't have*.

Example:

A Has Francis got back from Moscow yet?

B No, he hasn't. Apparently he was worried he wouldn't get to the airport in time.

A Oh, so I guess he *must have missed* (miss) the plane.

CONVERSATION 1 A I've just seen Carlos in the corridor carrying a bottle of champagne!

B I thought he was still negotiating with the Americans.

A Well, he [1] .... (get) the contract!

CONVERSATION 2 A Have you had any response from Sarah?

B No, I sent her an e-mail but it came back to me so she [2] .... (read) it.

CONVERSATION 3 A I don't understand it. Our competitors are already selling their new model and it's exactly the same as our prototype.

B Someone [3] .... (copy) the design and sold it to them.

A So who was it, do you think?

B Well, it [4] .... (be) anyone in my team because no one had access to the computer files.

A Somebody [5] .... (know) the password.

B Yes, it looks like it. But it [6] .... (be) at least six months ago.

A What was the name of that computer programmer who worked for us for a while and then left rather suddenly?

B The man with the little moustache?

---

2 🔲 Listen and check.

SPECULATING   What explanations can you give for the following?

1 I've tried ringing Anna all day but there's no answer.

2 I've just seen a lot of dead fish in the river next to the factory.

3 They've suddenly recalled all the models produced between April and June last year.

4 There's an angry group of workers carrying banners and placards outside the main factory entrance.

5 I can't understand how his personal secretary can have been promoted so quickly.

1 *She must have gone out.* ....

2 ....

3 ....

4 ....

5 ....

PRESENTATIONS Read through the article from a training manual and decide where the questions *A–J* should be.

TEN STEPS TOWARDS A SUCCESSFUL

PRESENTATION

Thinking about your audience is the key to good public speaking, writes Peter Stutt.
If you are preparing a presentation, start with this question: Who are these people?
It's the key to success. Whether they are strangers or colleagues, they have one thing in
common; they expect you to impress them for the next 15 or 20 minutes. And the best
way to do so is to focus on their favourite subject – themselves. So begin by defining who
these people are and what they expect. Here are ten questions to ask yourself.

A *What kind of language do these people use?*
B *Why were you invited to make this presentation?*
C *Can people hear you?*
D *How should you look at the audience?*
E *Should you use notes?*

F *Are they friends, colleagues, customers or total strangers?*
G *What work-related problems do these people have?*
H *Does the audience appreciate humour?*
I *Should you show any visual aids?*
J *How long should the presentation be?*

......F.... **1** *Define who these people are. Define their essential features and motivations. What work do they do, what is their level of education, what kind of language do they use, what problems and opportunities might they have?*

.... **2** *There must be something special about your expertise that is of interest to the audience. An audience can be disappointed if the speaker ignores the reason why he or she was chosen.*

.... **3** *When you were invited, you were probably given a general idea. The best thing is to take only as much time as is necessary. The only thing worse than being long and boring is being too short and not fully understood.*

.... **4** *Your knowledge of their problems is probably why you were invited to speak. They expect new insights, a different point of view, and ideas that they can take away and use so that they feel their time was well spent listening to you.*

.... **5** *If your audience is from a particular industry, what terminology does it understand best? The audience dictates your choice of words, but remember, you should always make your language clear and concise, especially if the language is not your mother tongue.*

.... **6** *Yes, but what is funny in one culture may not be in another. The subject of your presentation is probably serious and, for some people, humour may be out of place. A light touch here and there is all right but humour cannot replace good ideas.*

.... **7** *If they make your speech easier to understand, yes. But make them clear and simple. Don't laboriously read out aloud what is written on your OHTs. Make sure that everyone can see them, even from the back of the room.*

.... **8** *Speak loudly enough to make your voice carry to the furthest listener. No one wants to listen to someone who mumbles and who does not speak with conviction.*

.... **9** *Make direct eye contact. Try to convince your audience you are talking to them personally. It also makes you feel that you have made contact with them as individuals.*

.... **10** *Yes, make an outline, perhaps on small cards, and consult them as you speak. This forces you to organise your presentation in a logical, coherent way and not wander off the point.*

1 Read the text of the presentation below and predict where the speaker uses the linking words and expressions.

by and large   *therefore*   **whereas**   however
    although   **so**   in my opinion

Total Quality Assurance means meeting customer needs without error, on time, every time. Our experience so far has ¹ *by and large* been good. ² _____ , the message has not yet reached everybody in the company. ³ _____ the number of projects and people involved has grown, they have not grown as fast as we would like. ⁴ _____ , one of the key problems is how to express the benefits of this programme in money terms. ⁵ _____ , this problem is particularly acute when accounting for the less tangible benefits of the programme. At the shop floor level, people will tend to talk the language of things, ⁶ _____ at the upper management, people talk the language of money. Middle management, ⁷ _____ , need to be bilingual to translate between the two.

2 🔲 Listen and check.

3 Which of the linking expressions actually used in the speech could be replaced by those below?

consequently   *to my mind*
    now   **even so**   on the whole

■ *For more on linking words, go to page 134 of the Course Book.* ■

EMPLOYMENT IN EUROPE

Look at the following information about employment in Europe and prepare a short talk using these four headings:

- Unemployment patterns in the EU
- Unemployment in specific EU countries
- Working hours and average wages
- Job creation: the French experience

Unemployment 1950–95 as a percentage of the labour force

*Becoming European Union

	Youth unemployment Under 25s unemployed as a % of the active population, 1995	Working week Average usual f/t hours worked per week, 1996	Wages Hourly gross pay (£) adjusted for OECD 1996 purchasing parties
Belgium	24.4	38.3	9.4
Denmark	10.1	38.7	9.1
Germany	8.8	39.7	8.8
Greece	27.9	40.4	4.9
Spain	42.5	40.6	7.8
France	27.3	39.8	7.7
Ireland	19.5	40.4	8.3
Italy	33.2	38.6	7.3
Luxembourg	7.1	39.5	8.8
Netherlands	11.5	39.4	8.0
Austria	5.8	40.0	8.6
Portugal	16.8	41.2	3.5
Finland	38.2	38.7	7.4
Sweden	19.4	40.0	7.8
UK	15.9	43.9	8.3
EU average	21.5	40.3	7.7

Where the jobs aren't

Key

3.0 Unemployment as a % of total Labour force, April 1997

00.0 Long-term (1 year plus) unemployment as a % of total unemployed (1996 figures)

The Guardian, *7 October 1997*

The French experience

1981

Hours cut from 40 to 39

1m unemployed

In 1981, Pierre Mauroy's Socialist and Communist government cut the working week from 40 hours to 39. But an attempt to cut wages proportionately failed because of union opposition. The aim was to cut the 1m unemployment.

1997

Proposed further cut from 39 to 35

3.1m unemployed

Now there are 3.1m jobless. Lionel Jospin proposes to cut the working week to 35 hours without loss of pay over the next three years. His Socialist government says it will create 1.4m jobs.

RESPONDING TO INVITATIONS

Write a short reply for each invitation.

Mr Brian Coleman (Chairman)
and all the members of the Lion's Club

request the pleasure of the company of

David Wheeler

at a Banquet to be held at
The Beckett Hotel, Old Dover Road, Ashford
on Saturday 14 December at 8 pm.

Dear Mona,

Hello again! It seems ages since we last saw each other.

Maria and I are having a few friends round for a barbecue next Saturday and we were wondering if you would be able to make it. It's nothing special, but we thought it would be nice to get together again. I do know that John has got an idea in his head to organise an expedition in the foothills of the Himalayas, so be prepared!

Let us know if you can't come, otherwise we'll expect you at 8 for 8.30.

Carl

PS I almost forgot to tell you — we've moved!
The new address is:
Flat B, Spanish Court, 701 NW 13th Street,
Boca Raton.

CHECK YOUR PERFORMANCE

ECONOMICS

Complete the sentences with the words in the box. Use the dictionary entries if necessary.

economy economics **economic** *economical* economist

1 Many of the ideas that people fight over have _____ at their core.

2 A devaluation is not always the best solution to a country's _____ problems.

3 A collectivist _____ centralises power and often becomes bureaucratic and inefficient.

4 There's an increasing demand for small cars which are more _____ on fuel.

5 Adam Smith, who wrote *The Wealth of Nations*, was perhaps the first great modern _____ .

The adjective of the word **economy** [C], meaning the economy of a country is **economic**: *government measures to boost the economy\the various economies of South America\We are faced with a deepening economic crisis* (NOT *economical*.)*economic growth/benefits/problems/policy*

The study of economies and their money systems is called **economics** (singular): *He's got a degree in Modern History and Economics* (NOT *economic or economy*).*Economics is my favourite subject* (NOT *are my favourite subject*).

The adjective **economical** relates to the word **economy** meaning the careful use of money, a supply of something, effort etc that avoids any waste: *My new car is quite economical* (= cheap to run).*She was brought up to be economical with the housekeeping money* (= spend it carefully).

Something that is **economical** is not necessarily **cheap**. For example, it may be more economical to buy a packet of soap powder that is twice the usual size, because even though it costs more than the small packet, it does not cost twice the amount. However, sometimes people who sell things call **cheap** things **economical** simply because this word sounds better.

An **economist** is someone who studies the way in which money and goods are produced and used in the systems of business and trade.

SCORE: 5

PRESENTATIONS

Match the words and phrases with the different stages of a presentation.

1 If you look at the pie chart ...
2 Secondly, I'd like to look at ...
3 I'd like now to sum up the main points ...
4 I'm going to talk about ...
5 Let's now move on to a separate issue which is ...
6 First of all, let me welcome you to Digital Enterprises ...

a Greeting the audience
b Introducing the subject
c Sequencing
d Introducing a visual aid
e Changing the topic
f Concluding

SCORE: 5

ECONOMIC ORGANISATION

Read the statements and organise them into two groups: Advantages of nationalisation (*A*) and Disadvantages of nationalisation (*D*).

1 It provides essential but uneconomical services, for example, railway lines or postal services to remote areas.

2 Losses have to be met by taxpayers.

3 A country's wealth and jobs can be protected by its governing institutions.

4 Some strategic industries such as Atomic Energy and Defence are too important to be left in private hands.

5 The ultimate bosses are the politicians and political objectives may become more important than business sense.

6 The lack of competition can easily lead to inefficiency and waste.

7 Only a government has the resources to undertake vast capital equipment costs.

8 People will only work for their own self-interest not for the community as a whole.

9 Profits are for the benefit of the whole community rather than private individuals.

10 Central planning cannot provide fast, flexible reactions to changes in the business environment.

SCORE: 5   (0.5 for each correct answer)

DEDUCTIONS

Here are some facts and figures concerning the imaginary oil-producing country of Ruritania. Complete the sentences under each section using *must* or *can't*.

STATISTICS
Population: 1.8m
Gross Domestic Product: $7,400,000
Per capita income: $12,653
   (no personal income tax)

FOREIGN INVESTMENT
Freedom to repatriate profits
Modern infrastructure with good roads,
ports, airports and telecommunications

AGRICULTURE
Average temperature 28°-38°C
90% desert, very few farmers

LANGUAGES
Many local dialects;
English-medium
instruction in
universities.

GEOGRAPHY
Beautiful coastal landscapes
Ancient monuments in the desert

1 There .... be very many poor people.

2 Ruritania .... be a good place for a holiday.

3 Ruritania .... attract a lot of foreign capital.

4 They .... produce a lot of their own food.

5 Children .... be able to understand English.

SCORE: 5

A THANK YOU LETTER

Complete the letter by underlining the correct words in each case.

[1](I thank you/<u>Thank you</u>) very much for your kindness during my stay in New York [2](the last week/last week). I very much enjoyed [3](to hear/hearing) your views on the American market and the possibility of a joint venture. It was very kind of you to [4](put me up/put up me) for the night and I hope [5](to have/having) the opportunity to return your hospitality when we meet [6](ourselves/each other) again.

Best wishes,

SCORE: 5

TOTAL: 25

business ethics

SPECULATING ABOUT THE PAST

We can speculate about what didn't happen in the past by using *If* and the past perfect. We can also make a deduction by using *must have* + past participle.

Complete the following legal cases with the verbs in brackets.

Example:

Caxton plc, a printing firm, required new equipment and software to expand their business. They had accepted a number of contracts and had ordered the equipment from Dataserve plc. However, Caxton did not receive the equipment until after a three-week delay. Meanwhile, they lost their contracts to competitors.

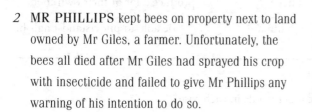

Caxton claims that if Dataserve *had delivered* (deliver) the equipment on time, they *would not have lost* (not lose) the contracts. And Dataserve *must have known* (know) that the delay would lead to loss of business.

1   **MRS LOTT** inherited £100,000 when her uncle died. She consulted her bank manager, Mr Wise, about the best way to invest the money and, on his advice, bought shares in the Kwikbrik construction company of which he was a director. Unfortunately, Kwikbrik went bankrupt three months later and Mrs Lott lost all her money.

If she _____ (know) about the state of the Kwikbrik company, she _____ (not invest) her money in it. She is now suing the bank because Mr Wise _____ (foresee) the company's bankruptcy.

2   **MR PHILLIPS** kept bees on property next to land owned by Mr Giles, a farmer. Unfortunately, the bees all died after Mr Giles had sprayed his crop with insecticide and failed to give Mr Phillips any warning of his intention to do so.

If Mr Giles _____ (tell) Mr Phillips of his intention, Mr Phillips _____ (remove) the bees. He is suing him because, as a farmer, Mr Giles _____ (realise) that the insecticide was dangerous.

3   **MR BUDD**, an antique dealer, acquired a rare first edition and wrote to Mrs Parsons, a rich book collector, who was sure to want it for her own library, offering to sell her it for £75,000. The next day a customer called Mr Quill offered him £90,000 for the manuscript and Mr Budd accepted.

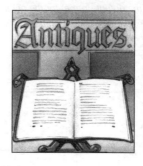

Mrs Parsons is now suing him for breach of promise because he _____ (be) aware that she would accept. But Mr Budd claims that if she _____ (inform) him she wanted to buy, he _____ (not sell) it to Mr Quill.

In 1997 the German firm Mercedes-Benz launched its new 'A Class' car. This small car was a significant departure from the firm's usual policy of producing big luxury cars. At first everything went well and the press was enthusiastic.

Mercedes-Benz
A CLASS

It is not often a new car marks a turning point in the industry. But that is the general view of Mercedes-Benz's 'A Class', which goes on sale soon.

The campaign to publicise the least conventional model in the range has won praise from advertising agencies as a case study on how to prepare the public for something unexpected without spoiling an up-market brand image.

Motoring journalists have also given the 'A Class' their backing, so much so that it seems certain to walk away with the 'European Car of the Year' Award.

Listen to a journalist from a motoring magazine describe what happened. Then choose the correct ending for each sentence.

1 After the incident on 23 September, the journalist would have
   a changed the tyres on the car.
   b stopped the launch to investigate the problem.
   c investigated the problem without stopping the launch.

2 After the incident on 21 October, he would have
   a explained that all cars behave in the same way.
   b held a press conference to tell everyone that the car is safe.
   c recalled all the models to the factory for safety checks.

3 Mercedes said it would
   a use a different make of tyre.
   b install a new safety device.
   c treat the incident as a joke.

Source: The Financial Times, September 1997

1 Before you read, think about these questions:

- Do you know where the shoes you are wearing were made?
- How much did they cost to buy?
- How much do you think they cost to make?

slavery in shoe factories

Millions of pairs of shoes sold on the UK's high streets are produced in the Third World under slave labour conditions, according to a report published yesterday.

1 The research highlights working conditions endured by thousands of workers in places such as China, Vietnam and Brazil, where child labour, poverty wages and health risks are common.

2 The report – Just How Clean Are Your Shoes? – has been prepared by the Catholic aid agency Cafod. It does not, however, want stores to boycott shoes produced in developing countries because this could lead to the closure of some factories, causing further poverty for workers.

3 Instead, it wants retailers to lay down tough rules to ensure overseas suppliers pay sufficient wages to meet basic needs, offer basic employment rights and refuse to use child labour. And it wants companies to employ independent inspectors to make manufacturers keep to their code of conduct.

4 British consumers spend £5 billion a year on 213 million pairs of shoes – and four out of five pairs are imported. Last year, one in every four pairs of shoes sold in the UK was made in China, where shoes can be produced for £1.77 a pair. It would cost £13.95 to make similar shoes in the UK. In some Chinese shoe factories, new workers can be paid 38p for a nine-hour day and up to a third may be deducted for board and lodging. Workers have only one or two rest days a month and three days holiday a year.

5 In Shenzen, China's booming enterprise zone just outside Hong Kong, Cafod found a factory employing children where there were no fire exits or fire extinguishers. Two years ago twenty workers died in a shoe factory in the same region.

6 Cafod highlights the punishment and humiliation to which some workers are subjected. It has reports of managers punishing workers for slow work by forcing them to kneel with their heads on the floor. In Brazil, women are regularly examined to make sure they are not pregnant when they apply for jobs. In one factory, workers were allowed only four minutes a day to use the lavatory.

7 Cafod is also worried about the health risks to workers, especially children, of using industrial glues and solvents without any ventilation or proper protection.

8 A spokesman for a British retail chain said the company 'passionately deplored the use of child labour' and frequently inspected suppliers' premises. It was considering toughening its code of conduct.

The Guardian, 12 September 1997

2 Answer the questions.

1 For what reasons are overseas suppliers criticised?

2 Why does Cafod not recommend boycotting factories in developing countries that employ child labour?

3 What does it recommend?

4 What proportion of shoes sold in the UK are made in the Third World?

5 What do you think the retail chain's code of conduct contains?

3 Which words in the article could be replaced by the following? The numbers refer to the paragraph in which the words occur.

1 points out (1) ....

2 place an embargo on (2) ....

3 stipulate (3) ....

4 accommodation (4) ....

5 flourishing (5) ....

6 strongly condemned (8) ....

7 reinforcing (8) ....

CHILD LABOUR IN BRITAIN

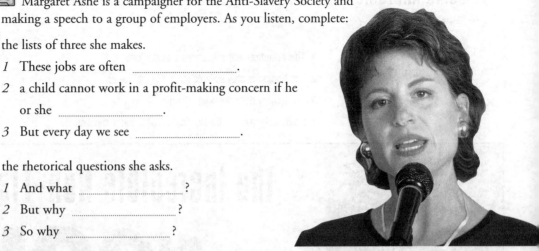 Margaret Ashe is a campaigner for the Anti-Slavery Society and is making a speech to a group of employers. As you listen, complete:

▪ the lists of three she makes.

1 These jobs are often ....

2 a child cannot work in a profit-making concern if he or she ....

3 But every day we see ....

▪ the rhetorical questions she asks.

1 And what .... ?

2 But why .... ?

3 So why .... ?

WRITING

1 Read the extract from a report produced by a well-known charity.

In one firm, we saw children as young as seven making footballs and shoes with the name of a famous football star on them. In another, we saw women and children in hot and humid conditions making sportswear for an international trade mark.

We are calling for a ban on all goods which are made using slave labour and for a policy of clear labelling that shows the country of origin and guarantees that the people who made them were treated fairly ...

2 You work as PR Officer for a company that employs workers in a number of Third World countries. You were recently criticised by a charitable organisation and wish to publish a justification of your own practices.

Use the following points to draft a letter that will be sent to newspapers such as *The Times*, *Le Monde, Die Zeit* and others.

▪ you do not employ children under 14
▪ rigorous inspection procedures to identify any under-age children
▪ published code of conduct
▪ difficult to judge age – lack of birth certificates in some areas

▪ many children undernourished – free food provided
▪ money earned necessary to support the family
▪ danger of imposing Western values on other countries
▪ employment better alternative than crime or prostitution

TOP GEAR

Dear Sir/Madam

I would like to point out, via your columns, that the recent criticism of our employment in the Third World is totally unjustified. First of all ...

1 Read the advertisement for the Nooksy Floor cleaner and decide whether these statements are true or false.

	T	F
▌ This advertisement announces a special offer.	☐	☐
▌ The Nooksy is only suitable for use in the home.	☐	☐
▌ The Nooksy does not need a plug.	☐	☐
▌ Disposable bags for the Nooksy can be found in most stores.	☐	☐

Exclusively to YOU for only £39.95

The Incredible Non-Electric

NOOKSY

Lifts out dirt with no fuss, no electricity, no noise.

NOOKSY is ideal for cleaning under furniture.

NOOKSY excels on carpets and hard floors.

The NOOKSY is the world's undisputed Number 1 floor cleaner because it cleans like no other cleaner can. And the less effort you use, the more effectively it cleans. Deep down clean.

Millions of people in airlines, hospitals, offices and restaurants all over the world will tell you how effective, how indispensable NOOKSY has become for them. Join the millions of satisfied NOOKSY owners for just £39.95 – no less than £10 off the manufacturer's recommended retail price.

With a NOOKSY you don't need to press down hard. As you sweep your NOOKSY along, its unique cleaning action generates static to attract almost anything on almost any surface. It effortlessly picks up dirt, pins and pet hair.

Once you've tried it, you'll wonder how you ever managed without it. And because it needs no electricity, it's completely free to run. There are no cables to trip over, no disposable bags to replace, no accessories to lose. It's the lightest, most efficient sweeper you can possibly buy.

Be good to yourself. Be good to your home.

2 Read the advertisement again and find similar examples of the language used.

Sound repetition	*picks up dirt, pins and pet hair; deep down clean*
Exaggeration	*the world's undisputed Number 1*
Parallels	*no fuss, no electricity, no noise*
Superlatives	*the lightest, most efficient sweeper you can buy*

GREED IS BAD

In his book *Maverick*, Ricardo Semler describes the organisation of a company in Brazil called *Semco* which is run on democratic principles. Workers participate fully in all types of decision-making and there is no rigid hierarchy (for example, they don't have an organisation chart). In particular, they decide their own rates of pay.

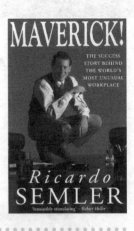

1 The following extract is an account of the interview Ricardo had with one of the employees. Before you read, think about these questions:

- Do you think you are paid too much or too little?
- How much would you pay yourself for the job you do at present?

We were aware that, if we allowed people to set their own salaries, the differences among colleagues could become irritating and disruptive. Conventional salary systems, after all, strive for standardisation. The system we were contemplating would be individualistic. Executives would be called on to make difficult distinctions of worth and value. What if someone lacked the experience of a colleague, but considered himself more dynamic? If an executive asked for too little and got it, would he be undervalued by those around him?

I called in Irene Tubertini, one of my three secretaries. 'How much money do you need to earn to live comfortably?' I asked her. 'How much money do you need so that you will leave for work in the morning with the feeling that you are fairly paid, so that you won't be tempted to look for another job?'

She sat there, not quite believing what she was hearing, wondering what I could possibly be up to. I told her to think about it for a day or two, then give me a number. That would be her salary for the next year. 'Yes, I was serious,' I told her. We intended to ask others the same question, and hold them to their answers.

A few days later Irene told me she wanted to be paid $20,000 a year, which was a shade higher than she had been making. That seemed a little low to me, so I pushed it up by ten per cent and we had a deal.

▌ GLOSSARY ▌

strive   *make an effort towards*
lacked   *did not have*

2 Answer the questions.

1 What were the dangers of allowing people to set their own salaries?

....

2 What was Irene's initial reaction towards deciding her own rate of pay?

....

3 Was her figure the same as Ricardo's?

....

3 According to this extract, what does Ricardo think remuneration should be based on? Tick those that are justified by the passage.

- an employee's seniority
- an employee's previous experience
- an employee's family needs

- an employee's dynamism and creativity
- a sense of fairness
- a fixed sum for people in the same category

ETHICAL VOCABULARY

Add *un*, *im*, *in*, *dis*, or *il* to the words to make the opposite meaning.

1 truthful   *untruthful*

2 fair   ....   5 moral   ....

3 honest   ....   6 legal   ....

4 decent   ....

SCORE: 5

THIRD CONDITIONAL

Join the sentences using the third conditional.

1 We didn't anticipate market trends. We lost market share.

  If we had anticipated market trends, we wouldn't have lost market share.

2 They didn't listen to the union demands. There was a strike.

  If ....

3 We introduced job rotation. People learnt different skills.

  If ....

4 She had a headache. Her presentation was poor.

  If ....

5 He bribed a ministry official. He got the contract.

  If ....

6 We increased our prices. We lost market share.

  If ....

■ *For more on the third conditional, go to page 130 of the Course Book.* ■

SCORE: 5

PRESENTATIONS

Match the different parts of the presentation with the phrases.

1 I'd like to give you an example ...   *a* a general idea
2 To move off the point for a moment ...   *b* a visual aid
3 Let's have a look at this chart which represents ...   *c* a digression
4 What I want to make clear is this ...   *d* an example
5 I'd just like to give you an overview of ...   *e* an important idea
6 What I really want to stress is this ...   *f* a point of clarification

SCORE: 5

INVITATIONS AND OFFERS

Match the sentences with the appropriate group.

1 Would you like one?
2 Thank you.
3 That suits me fine.
4 I am very much obliged.
5 How about a round of golf?
6 This is a small token of our appreciation.
7 I'm afraid I've made other arrangements.
8 I'm sorry but I'm not authorised to accept this.
9 I was wondering if you would like tickets for the opera.
10 We thought your wife would like to receive this diamond bracelet.
11 That is very kind of you but I have to turn you down on this occasion.

Invitations and offers
1

Acceptances

Refusals

SCORE: 5   (0.5 for each correct answer)

GIVING GIFTS   Order the sentences to reconstitute the story.

There is a story that the former president of the USA, Lyndon B. Johnson, once embarrassed the president of Mexico. He offered the Mexican a gift when he had nothing to give in return.

A   **1**

A camel trader, Abdel-Wahah Waguih, was so honoured that he not only gave Carter a guided tour but also presented him with several Sudanese camel whips and a six-year-old camel with a pink ribbon round its neck.

B

To avoid any similar embarrassment, Johnson instructed his secret service agents always to carry Accutron watches in their pockets. In this way he would never be caught empty-handed himself.

C

Another American president, Jimmy Carter, was visiting Cairo and asked to see the local camel market.

D

However, American officials intervened and told him not to. They said that the president probably would not like it.

E

But his generosity did not stop there. He also wanted to further honour the president by killing a camel at his feet.

F

SCORE: 5

TOTAL: 25

10 the **digital revolution**

THE INFORMATION SOCIETY

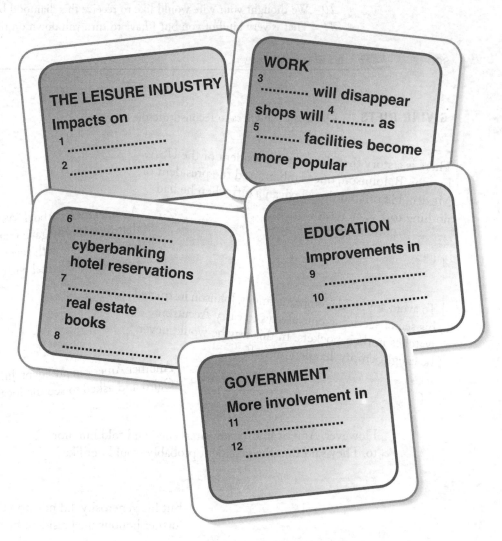 Listen to a presentation by David Knight, the Chief Information Officer of Softcell, an information systems consultancy. As you listen, fill in the slides.

THE LEISURE INDUSTRY

Impacts on

1 ....

2 ....

WORK

3 .... will disappear

shops will 4 .... as

5 .... facilities become

more popular

6 ....

cyberbanking
hotel reservations

7 ....

real estate
books

8 ....

EDUCATION

Improvements in

9 ....

10 ....

GOVERNMENT

More involvement in

11 ....

12 ....

REPORTED SPEECH

Match the direct speech in quotation marks with the reported speech.

1 'Don't forget to save your file.'
2 'I'm sorry, I didn't save the file.'
3 'If I were you, I'd save the file now.'
4 'I'll save the file for you now.'
5 'I wish I had saved the file.'

a She offered to save the file.
b She reminded me to save the file.
c She regretted not saving the file.
d She apologised for not saving the file.
e She suggested I save the file.

■ *For more on reported statements, go to page 145 of the Course Book.* ■

EFFECTIVE WRITING In the essay *Politics and The English Language*, George Orwell 'translates' a passage from the Bible into 'modern English of the worst sort'. Note how simple words have been badly rewritten into complicated abstract language.

> I returned and saw under the sun, that the race is not to the swift, nor the battle to the strong, neither yet bread to the wise, nor yet riches to men of understanding, nor yet favour to men of skill; but time and chance happeneth to them all.

> Objective considerations of contemporary phenomena compels the conclusion that success or failure in competitive activities exhibits no tendency to be commensurate with innate capacity, but that a considerable element of the unpredictable must invariably be taken into account.

1 Match the simple statements below with their translations into 'English of the worst sort'.

a Demographic profiles of the inhabitants of nation states within the European Union indicate that the segment of the population beyond retirement age enjoys greater personal disposable income than any generation of senior citizens that preceded them.

b The main difficulty with which we find ourselves faced at present is whether it is advisable for our firm to invest in an improved facility for generating hard copy of documents or whether, on balance, it would seem to be more advisable to maintain the status quo.

c It is not uncommon for people who are under the obligation to endure repeated and continuous exposure to music played at excessive levels of decibels to suffer a degree of impairment in their auditory faculty.

1 People often go a bit deaf if the music is too loud.

2 In Europe, people over 65 are richer than ever.

3 We don't know whether to invest in a new printer or not.

2 Rewrite the following sentences so that the message is expressed more clearly and is no longer in 'English of the worst sort'.

1 The machine which is employed to reproduce text and image-based copies has ceased to function.

> **The photocopier isn't working.**

2 I hereby acknowledge receipt of the document I have received from you by the process of facsimile transmission.

3 In my opinion, it is a conclusion with which I would not disagree.

4 Visitors are kindly reminded that they should position their vehicles in the area that has been specifically designed for their temporary use.

5 In order to improve the performance of employees and ensure that their working practices are as efficient as is humanly possible, a manager needs to make sure that they have adequate and sufficient training to undertake the tasks assigned to them.

1 Read the two articles about a number of technological developments. Answer the questions.

1 What does a NVT enable people to do?

....

2 Who is it likely to appeal to?

....

3 Why is it likely to appeal to them?

....

4 What does the writer think about it?

....

5 What does AOL stand for?

....

6 What is the 'problem' referred to?

....

7 How often does this type of problem occur?

....

8 What is the cause of this problem?

....

NVT: A better use of time?

1 IBM, Netscape, Sun Microsystems and Delco have joined forces to create a Network Vehicle of Tomorrow (NVT).

2 The idea is to enable commuters to use their time better. Drivers can verbally request and listen to e-mail messages being read out loud. They can dictate memos and electronically distribute them, request sports scores or music, or ask for directions to a specific location.

3 All this while keeping their eyes, if not their minds, on the road.

4 The car was a show stopper in Las Vegas, but it says more about the lifestyles of Silicon Valley techies than future market trends.

5 To find affordable housing, many of the region's engineers and programmers live long distances from their places of work. Most commute alone for an hour or more on increasingly congested highways. Being 'off-line' – or disconnected from the internet – is the biggest frustration they face while stuck in traffic.

6 The rest of us may be happy to while away our commute hours listening to a local radio station or making phone calls, but for true digital citizens it is painful to be disconnected for so long.

7 Their e-mail, I have to assume, is a lot more compelling than mine.

The Financial Times, *19 November 1997*

AOL's E-Mail Service Is Brought Down by Software Bug

1 'You've got mail!' chirps the familiar electronic voice when America Online users sign on. But lately, retrieving that mail has been a less-than-chirpy experience.

2 A five-hour e-mail blackout during business hours in the continental US last week left customers of America Online Inc. incommunicado and frustrated. It was the third outage in three weeks, and this one occurred just as AOL was bragging that it had reached a milestone: signing up its ten millionth customer.

3 And that could be the root of the problem. AOL now has about 530,000 simultaneous users on its system during peak hours, up from 140,000 a year ago. One of their favourite activities is sending e-mail, a medium that's expanding faster than the on-line industry's ability to handle it.

4 'They brag about having 10 million customers – but 9,999,999, of them are dissatisfied' grumbles AOL subscriber Lou Ganim of Clifton Park, New York. Travelling on business last week, he left behind an important file but figured it was no problem – he asked a co-worker to send it to his American Online account last Monday night. He logged on to AOL Tuesday morning and was miffed to learn the company's entire electronic-mail system had crashed.

Wall Street Journal Europe, *26 November 1997*

2 Find the words with similar meanings to these words. The numbers refer to the paragraphs where you will find the word.

Financial Times

1 to permit (2)   *enable*

2 a huge success (4)

3 at a reasonable price (5)

4 to travel from home to work and back (5)

5 crowded or blocked (5)

6 spend time in a lazy or relaxed way (6)

7 interesting and persuasive (7)

Wall Street Journal

8 to make a short high-pitched sound like a bird (1)

9 getting access to (1)

10 happy (1)

11 unable to get in touch (2)

12 boasting (2)

13 cause (3)

14 thought (4)

15 e-mail address (4)

16 upset (4)

EDITING   The following e-mail is written in an inappropriate style and contains a lot of redundant language. Rewrite it in a more economical way.

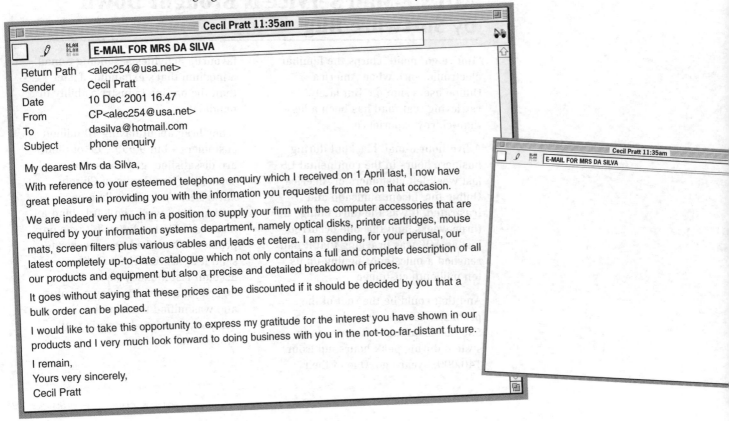

COMPUTER-BASED TRAINING   Listen to the meeting about computer-based training (CBT). Then complete the note a colleague sent to another colleague who had been unable to attend. Use the verbs in the box.

admitted   *agreed*   **maintained**

pointed out   promised   *reminded*

suggested   wondered

Dear Marianne

This is just a short note to let you know what was discussed at last Monday's meeting.

First, Francis Knight [1] ....*pointed out*.... that CBT was a lot less expensive than traditional classroom instruction. Betty Taylor [2] .... that this was true but [3] .... us that many of our key people just don't want to sit in front of a screen with a CD tutor. She also [4] .... whether the savings were really as great as people claimed. Terry Barker [5] .... to provide us with some statistics.

According to Betty, some forms of CBT like personal communication skills were much better done with a live teacher. Francis [6] .... this was true but [7] .... that CBT was more cost-effective in the majority of cases and [8] .... that we contact companies that had invested in multimedia training packages and ask their opinion.

Karen

A WEB PAGE **1** Read the information pages created by Cadbury on the world wide web. Match the pictures with the text.

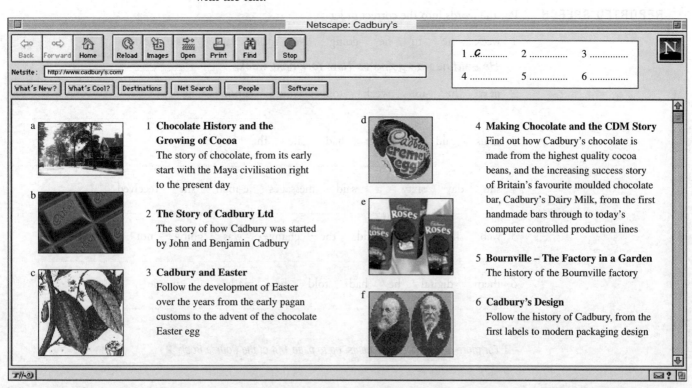

2 The information on the Story of Cadbury Ltd page has been put into the wrong order. Put the story back into the correct chronological sequence and insert the dates in the box.

1824   *1831*   **1860**   **1879**   **1899**

a

1866 saw a turning point for the company with the introduction of a process for pressing the cocoa butter from the cocoa beans. This enabled Cadbury Brothers to make new kinds of eating chocolate.

b

Cadbury today is the market leader in the UK chocolate confectionery market, employing the most advanced processing technology and management information and control techniques.

c

In ¹ *1899* the business became a private limited company – Cadbury Brothers Limited. Chocolate moved from being a 'luxury' item to being well within the financial reach of everyone.

d

By ² .... , the business had changed from a grocery shop and John Cadbury had become a manufacturer of drinking chocolate and cocoa. This was the start of the Cadbury manufacturing business as it is known today. John Cadbury was joined by his brother, Benjamin, and the business became a partnership, Cadbury Brothers of Birmingham. This partnership dissolved in ³ .... and a year later John Cadbury retired, leaving his sons Richard and George to continue the business.

1 e

A one-man retail business opened, in ⁴ .... by John Cadbury, in Birmingham was to be the foundation of Cadbury Limited, now one of the world's largest producers of chocolate.

f

Business prospered and Cadbury Brothers moved in ⁵ .... to a 'greenfield' site some miles from the centre of Birmingham which came to be called Bournville, the 'factory in a garden'.

CHECK YOUR PERFORMANCE

REPORTED SPEECH   Put the words into the correct order.

1 week   he   to   he   going   New York   said   was   next

He said he was going to New York next week.

2 next   he   me   week   told   would   phone   he

....

3 virus   said   computer   had   she   the   a

....

4 she   day   sixty   a   said   messages   e-mail   she   received

....

5 web   he   world   said   the   change   was   going   not   to   the

....

6 them   digital   he   had   told   he   made   a   movie

....

■ *For more on reported statements, go to page 144 of the Course Book.* ■

SCORE: 5

PREPOSITIONS   Fill in the spaces with the prepositions.

down   *up*   *in*   *on*   *up*   *in*

1 I have decided to trade-*in* my car for a newer model.

2 I've decided to .... grade my computer system and get a more powerful model.

3 With a modem you can .... load information from a central server.

4 Electronic commerce enables the consumer to buy goods and services .... -line.

5 They're selling televisions with built-................ internet access.

6 It's essential to make a back-................ copy of important files.

SCORE: 5

NOUN COMBINATIONS

Look at the groups of nouns. Tick those which are correct. Correct those which sound strange.

1 a network of telephone ☐ *a telephone network*
2 a words processor ☐ ....
3 a mobile phone ☐ ....
4 customer needs ☐ ....
5 a customer's needs ☐ ....
6 a software of package ☐ ....
7 maintenance costs ☐ ....
8 an instruction's manual ☐ ....
9 network management ☐ ....
10 the flow of information ☐ ....
11 Thomas Watson, the IBM founder ☐ ....

■ *For more on nouns in groups, go to page 136 of the Course Book.* ■

SCORE: 10

SOCIAL SKILLS

Choose the most appropriate thing you could say in each situation.

1 You have bumped into someone in the street. What could you say?
   a I beg your pardon very much.
   b Excuse me.
   c Sorry.

2 You are at a restaurant with an English-speaking customer. The waiter brings you the food you have ordered. What could you say?
   a Enjoy yourself.
   b Good appetite.
   c This looks good.

3 You want to leave a reception early. What could you say to the person you are talking to?
   a It was nice meeting you.
   b Thank you for having me.
   c I'm sorry it's been a pleasure.

4 Someone you know and like is going away for a long time. What could you say?
   a Go away!
   b All the best!
   c Pleased to see you go!

5 You want to attract a waiter's attention in a restaurant. What could you say?
   a Come here, waiter.
   b Waiter.
   c Please, sir.

SCORE: 5

TOTAL: 25

Powerhouse *transcript*

1 connections

ANSWERING THE PHONE (page 6)

1

OPERATOR International Directory Enquiries. Can I help you?

CALLER Yes. I'd like the telephone number of someone in the United States, please.

OPERATOR Yes, which state?

CALLER Louisiana.

OPERATOR And the name?

CALLER Todd Whatley.

OPERATOR Could you spell that for me, please?

CALLER W H A T L E Y.

OPERATOR Right. And the name of the city?

CALLER Baton Rouge.

OPERATOR And the spelling of 'Baton'?

CALLER B A T O N.

OPERATOR T or D?

CALLER T for Tango.

OPERATOR T. OK. That's Baton Rouge. I've got it. Todd Whatley. 701 North West 13th Street. 504 417 4820.

CALLER 504 417 4820. Thank you.

OPERATOR You're welcome.

JOHN Hello.

PENNY John.

JOHN Yeah. Penny, Hi!

PENNY Do you remember the name of the software specialist who spoke to us last week?

JOHN The one from Millennium Software, in Vancouver?

PENNY Millennium Software, that's right.

JOHN It was Sophie Baylen, I think. Wait a minute, I've got it written down here somewhere. Yeah, here we are, Sophie Baylen, B A Y L E N.

PENNY And have you got her number?

JOHN Yeah, it's 223 8515, and the area code is 250.

2

RECEPTIONIST Docklands Exhibition Centre. Can I help you?

CALLER Yes, I'd like to speak to Mr Turner, please.

RECEPTIONIST Yes. Who's calling, please?

CALLER Mr Mead from Digital Electronics.

RECEPTIONIST Hold the line, please. I'm sorry he's not in at the moment. Can I take a message?

CALLER Yes, please. Could you tell him to get in touch with Mr Robert Mead, that's M E A D, from Digital Electronics as soon as possible. It's very important.

RECEPTIONIST And the telephone number?

CALLER It's 01865 502316, extension 99.

RECEPTIONIST So that's Mr Mead on 01865 502316, extension 99. I'll make sure he gets your message.

CALLER Thank you very much.

RECEPTIONIST Hello. Sales department.

CALLER Yes, hello, my name is Linda Burne. I saw the advertisement for your products and I'd like to speak to your sales manager.

RECEPTIONIST Yes, can you tell me your name again?

CALLER Yes, Linda Burne, B U R N E, and I work for SCI International.

RECEPTIONIST Right, I'm afraid our sales manager is visiting a client this afternoon. Is there a number she can contact you on when she gets back?

CALLER Yes, 0181 442 5655 and I'm on extension 39.

RECEPTIONIST Right, I've got that and she'll be getting in touch with you soon. Thank you for your call.

2 the company

FOCUS ON COMPANIES (page 15)

A large number of recent take-overs in Europe, many of them cross-border deals, will keep anti-trust officials at the European Commission busy for months to come.

FERRIER of France, the second-biggest cement maker in the world, has announced a friendly £1.7 billion bid for Britain's REDSTONE, the maker of tiles and aggregates.

The proposed £240 million merger between Britain's SUN-UP and THE METRO GROUP, which was to have created the world's largest drinks maker, will now not take place. CORDA, a maker of luxury goods with an interest in Sun-up, has now made an increased offer of £250 million.

GENERAL PROTECTION and UCP are to merge in a £14.1 billion deal to create one of Europe's biggest insurance and asset management groups. The combined business will be a major player in life assurance with a significant presence in the UK, Canada, the US and continental Europe.

The new company, to be called GCP, will be Britain's second-biggest insurer and rank ninth in Europe.

The company has announced that its US headquarters will be in Boston, where UCP's head office is already located. 2,000 people are expected to lose their jobs in the UK as a result of the merger.

3 money

FINANCIAL NEWS (page 20)

REPORTER In the City today investors were in a buoyant mood and share prices soared as the FTSE 100 index, up 14 points at one stage, closed 10.4 higher at 5211.6. Here to tell us about it is our financial correspondent, Jeremy Barnes.

BARNES Most commentators agree that the economy is now likely to grow at a rate of over 3% per year. However, some experts also forecast trouble ahead for the government's borrowing strategy and uncertainty for inflation. But today, investors were more concerned with interest rates – particularly American ones, which have kept others high all round the world. The official American discount rate – their bank rate – came down at the weekend so Wall St raced up this morning and again this afternoon with the Dow Jones Index up 12 points to 8030.

REPORTER Thank you, Jeremy. And here is the rest of the Financial News. On a bullish stock market today, despite a loss for Associated Metals, down 5 at 426, there were gains for the RZT Group at 288, up 2 and British Fuels, up 4 at 208. WTC rose 3 at 74, Courtman's edged up 1 at 55 and GLX increased by 11 points to close at 692. Smith & Parker, however, closed down 4 at 66 on a disappointing profits recovery. But the news of the day was the announcement of Transpax's successful £40 million bid for the take-over of the Huntingdon group – their shares finished a hefty 130 up at 219.

Finally, the pound closed up 1.4 cents at one dollar fifty-seven cents but it was down by 3 German pfennigs. Even so, Sterling's overall international value was up 0.2 at 88.9% of its 1998 level.

That's all for tonight and we hand you over to Samuel Palmer for a look at how governments are dealing with the problems of global warming …

CALCULATIONS (page 22)

Calculation 1

So just let me try and work that out. Our gross profit is $120 per packet, and we aim to sell 50,000 packets in all, so 50,000 multiplied by 120 makes $6 million gross profit. But of course we'll be spending $2.5 million on advertising so 6 minus 2.5 equals 3.5 million.

Calculation 2

Of course there's the rent for the site, that amounts to £7,415; wages – that's £13,350 and other overheads of, we estimate at £60,050, which in all comes to …

Calculation 3

Well, according to my calculations, our fixed costs are £22,500 and our variable costs exactly £10 per unit. Now, if in year 1 we sell 3,000 units, our variable costs will be 3,000 multiplied by 10. That's £30,000. Add to that the fixed costs. That makes a total of £52,500 and on the basis of a sales income of £15 per unit, we should make £45,000.

In year 2 we could double sales, so our variable costs would be £60,000 and total costs £82,500. Sales income would be twice £45,000 so that makes £90,000.

So if you look at the break even chart for year 2 and draw a line representing sales income from zero to 90,000 and another line representing total costs from 22,500 to 82,500 for the same period, we can calculate the break-even point, which is where the two lines intersect. In this case, the break-even point is … well, I'll let you calculate it for yourselves.

5 management

OXFORD BUSINESS BRIEFS (page 38)

INTERVIEWER Some people in Oxford have captured an unusual export market. Oxford Business Briefs provide daily information bulletins to clients in international business. Their most important market is the United States because of the time difference. Top people there can wake up and have the daily brief waiting for them when they get to the office. The analyses come from a mixture of international experts from about forty universities around the world.

But who exactly, I wondered, are their customers? I asked the founder of Oxford Business Briefs, Dr David Young.

DR YOUNG The main clients are the big banks, oil companies, manufacturing multinationals, and so on. It's very interesting in that we originally conceived the idea as going into the chief executive's office – that has been true and there are many top executives who are getting the briefs. But it's clear that throughout these corporations they've found a whole variety of uses – for strategic planning managers or the money managers. For example, one of the big banks in New York has a screen in the middle of the trading room and the traders can all look at it first thing in the morning.

INTERVIEWER But couldn't these big corporations involved in worldwide affairs find this information elsewhere?

DR YOUNG That's a good question and that was one of the key questions we had to address when we set up. Basically, our briefs are less journalistic than the worldwide news agencies. They're more analytical. Each brief is divided into four parts: the title, the significance, the analysis and then the conclusion. We think this is the best way to do it because business audiences and senior management just don't have the time to read large amounts of text. So we give them the essential information in a very concise format. The whole idea was to say, 'could we do in the private sector what Presidents, Prime Ministers and Cabinet members get from their staff on a daily basis?'

INTERVIEWER I asked one of their clients, Scott Walker of Atlantic Richfield, what proportion of the briefs that he received he found specifically useful.

SCOTT WALKER We found 40% useful and relevant, 35% marginal and 25% irrelevant to our needs.

INTERVIEWER And did you pass that information back?

SCOTT WALKER We sure did and they were interested in that and compared our results with those of other client companies of theirs and I haven't seen the total results yet but I understand that what's often useful to us is not useful to other clients and vice versa.

INTERVIEWER Dr Young?

DR YOUNG It's hard to know in advance what subjects clients will be interested in. But we just have to trust our own judgement. Actually, I had breakfast the other day with a senior official in Washington. And he'd just been reading the Oxford Business Brief on trade prospects in the former Soviet Union. And he said that he thought it was the best thing he'd read on the subject and that, I think, was a pretty good tribute.

DEVELOPING A CONVERSATION (page 41)

RICHARD Did I tell you that I had an interview for that job that was advertised in *The Times*?

TONY No, I don't think so.

RICHARD Well, I got the job.

TONY Oh really! Well done!

RICHARD But I didn't take it.

TONY Oh? Why not?

RICHARD A number of things really. The job was in central London and you know what it's like coming in on the train every day.

TONY Yeah. You bet I do.

RICHARD And the salary they were offering wasn't fantastic, less than what I'm on now.

TONY Right.

RICHARD On the other hand, the job itself was interesting, with the possibility of lots of travel in the Far East.

TONY Mmm.

RICHARD But then again I didn't really want to leave Carol on her own with the children and she's in the middle of a reorganisation at work.

TONY No. I see what you mean. Still, it's a pity about the salary because ...

6 the customer

BARGAINING (page 47)

A So, to recapitulate, if you purchase a second machine from us then we'll pay for delivery.

B Yes, that might be acceptable but only on condition that you agree to an extra 5% discount. If you can do that then we have a deal.

A No, I'm afraid that's out of the question. We're already offering as low a price as we can. But if you like, as a gesture on our part and to show our goodwill, we could, in addition to the free delivery, allow you an extra 1.5% but that's as far as we can go.

B 1.5%. No, that really isn't enough. Our previous supplier always gave us 5%. And free maintenance. We need that.

A Um, well, I'll make one final concession but I must be crazy. I think we can reach agreement on a discount of 2.5%, plus an extended warranty period of eighteen months. I can't do better than that so that really does have to be our final offer.

B OK. I think we may have a deal there if we split the difference and make it 3.75% and if you guarantee that the maintenance will be on-site because we can't afford to allow any ...

7 production

TOPICS OF CONVERSATION (page 57)

Conversation 1

A What are kippers?

B Kippers? They're fish, a kind of smoked herring. People sometimes have them for breakfast in England.

Conversation 2

A I've got two. One's at college doing business studies and the other's just got married, in fact, and she's gone to live in Finland. How about you?

B Well, my eldest wants to be a fashion designer ...

Conversation 3

A What places do you recommend while I'm here in Paris?

B Oh, you must go to the Seurat exhibition.

A Where's that on?

B At the Grand Palais.

Conversation 4

A Do you think interest rates will go down?

B Sooner or later, but I'm not sure when. Our rates are a lot higher than the rest of Europe.

A Yes, I suppose that's true ...

Conversation 5

A So what was the score?

B Well, it was two-all after extra time and they had to have one of those sudden death penalty shoot-outs.

A On no, I hate those. I think they're very unfair.

B Yes, so anyway one of the Juventus players missed a penalty which means that Bayern have gone through to the next round.

9 business ethics

LEARNING FROM THE PAST (page 69)

INTERVIEWER So what happened during the 'Car of the Year' tests?

JOURNALIST Well, the car showed a tendency to roll when swerving between objects placed on the road. What was particularly spectacular was that sometimes two wheels were off the ground. And, of course, these pictures were flashed around the world and made it look as if the 'A Class' was unsafe.

INTERVIEWER So what would you have done if you had been in charge of public relations?

JOURNALIST Well, there were a number of options. They could have done nothing. After all, Mercedes had devoted years of research and thousands of kilometres of testing to the new design. They could have explained that the way the car was being driven would mean that any car would behave in the same way. Or they could have stopped the launch and looked into the problem, if there was a problem.

INTERVIEWER What would you have done?

JOURNALIST I think I would have tried to find out the source of the problem but I wouldn't have stopped the launch at that stage.

INTERVIEWER And then as I understand it, a month later, on 21 October, five Swedish journalists caused a real crisis by turning the 'A Class' car over at just 60 kilometres an hour and one of the journalists was injured. What would you have done then?

JOURNALIST Well, that seemed to be more serious. Again, there were a number of choices. I could have done nothing and accused the journalists of not being serious test drivers. Or I could have held a press conference to explain how safe the car is. Alternatively, I could have recalled all the models due to go on sale to the factory and done some more tests.

INTERVIEWER What would you have done this time?

JOURNALIST I'd have called the press conference and this is what they did. On 29 October, the company invited journalists to its headquarters in Stuttgart and announced that the car should not be used with a certain kind of soft tyre. They said they would install as standard, and at no extra cost, an Electronic Stability Programme. However, a Swedish journalist who had been in the car said 'I lost control of the car. Without warning it turned over and hurt my colleague.'

CHILD LABOUR IN BRITAIN (page 71)

There are over two million young children who do some kind of paid work in Britain today. And what kind of work is it, ladies and gentlemen? These jobs are often underpaid, illegal and dangerous.

But why do young people do these jobs? Well, often because their parents put pressure on them to work to help pay the family bills. We think this is wrong. And the law says it's wrong too. The law says a child cannot work in a profit-making concern if he or she is under thirteen, is supposed to be at school or works for more than two hours at a time. But every day we see children working on farms, selling flowers or cleaning car windscreens in the street.

So why do I feel concerned? I'll tell you why …

10 the digital revolution

THE INFORMATION SOCIETY (page 76)

In the very near future, life as we know it will be very different. I'd like to focus on five major areas: The Leisure Industry; Work; Trading; Education and Government.

First of all, leisure will be very different. This will impact on two main areas: Travel and Entertainment. On-line services will provide people with rail and air tickets as well as with their home entertainment. There will be no need to rent videos, go to the cinema or buy CDs because these can all be downloaded from the internet.

Work will be different. The digital age is having a profound impact on jobs. Over 100,000 jobs in insurance will disappear in the next few years. In the retail sector, it is likely that some shops will close as on-line shopping facilities become more popular.

Thirdly, trading will be different. Already for many companies 10% of total sales are made over the internet. And we are likely to see an explosion in cyberbanking, hotel reservations, theatre ticket sales, real estate, books and sports goods.

In the field of education, information technology will improve both quality and access. Students will no longer be restricted to one particular location and will have access to the libraries of the world for the price of a local telephone call.

Finally, it is possible that information technology will change the way people interact in the democratic process. It is likely that they will become more involved in decision-making at all levels and we will see a new form of electronic democracy with much greater participation in local and national issues.

COMPUTER-BASED TRAINING (page 80)

KNIGHT .... one of the things we should realise is that CBT, computer-based training, is cheaper; you pay about 20% of the price of a traditional course and that's not including travel and accommodation if people have to go away.

TAYLOR OK, I don't deny that but what I'm saying is that a lot of our senior management just don't want to sit in front of a computer; they want to work with a real person. And in any case, I think your figures are a bit exaggerated.

BARKER If you like, I'll get hold of some facts and figures. I've got a friend who's done some research into this.

TAYLOR That'd be really good. I mean, I really think that you can't use a CD Rom or e-mail discussion groups or whatever for some kinds of training. What about presentations or interpersonal skills, for example?

KNIGHT Well, you've got a point but I still feel that most of the time you're going to spend less money if you invest in computer-based training. So what I think we ought to do is to get in touch with some firms that are in the same line of business as ourselves and ask them what they think.

answer key

1 connections

JOB DESCRIPTIONS

2 Jacob Kastor works as a human resources manager for RGA International Ltd. At the moment, he is implementing quality assessment procedures.

3 Carol Farih works as a marketing co-ordinator for DELTACOM. At the moment, she is launching a new range of up-market products.

4 Jean-Marie Barrault works as a financial manager for Argenton plc. At the moment, he is preparing next year's budget.

MODERN BRITAIN

2	is growing	*6*	is rebuilding
3	are expanding	*7*	is pulling down
4	is embarking	*8*	are rising
5	is building		

A PHONE BOX

2 What are you doing in England?
3 I'm attending a conference ...
4 ... and I are staying with some friends here.
5 She's doing some shopping.
6 You know Maria ...
7 ... every time we come to Cambridge.
8 ... she spends hours in bookshops.
9 I remember the last time ...
10 How long are you planning / do you plan to stay?
11 We're having a dinner party ...
12 We never eat before then.

ANSWERING THE PHONE

1
NAME:	TODD WHATLEY	NAME:	SOPHIE BAYLEN
CITY:	BATON ROUGE	CITY:	VANCOUVER
TEL NO:	504 417 4820	TEL NO:	223 8515 (area code 250)

2 Mr Mead, Digital Electronics
01865 502316, ext 99 (Urgent)

Linda Burne, SCI International
0181 442 5655, ext 39 (Can wait)

PHONE WORDS

toll free number   conference call   phone card   collect call
free phone number   phone number

A PHONE JUMBLE

10 **GOULD** Right. Well, thank you for your call.
1 **RECEPTIONIST** Parsons Engineering. Can I help you?
8 **GOULD** Yes, they've just been dispatched by DCL Courier and should get to you by tomorrow morning. If there's any problem, then just get back to me.
3 **RECEPTIONIST** I'm afraid he's on another line at the moment. Would you like to hold or can I take a message?
7 **SULLIVAN** Hello. My name is Michael Sullivan of Global Engines. I've been trying to get through to you. I'm calling to find out whether the spare parts I ordered last week have been sent off.
5 **RECEPTIONIST** Mr Gould is free now. I'm putting you through.
4 **SULLIVAN** No, it doesn't matter. I'll hold.
2 **SULLIVAN** Hello, this is Michael Sullivan of Global Engines. Could I speak to Mr Gould in Customer Services, please?
11 **SULLIVAN** Thank you. Goodbye.
9 **SULLIVAN** Oh good. Yes, OK, but I hope it won't be necessary.
6 **GOULD** Hello. Bill Gould.

THE ALPHABET

1 B, C, D, E, G, P, T, V, Z (pronounced 'zee' in American English, 'zed' in British English)
2 I, Y
3 O
4 A, H, J, K
5 Q, U, W
6 R

CULTURE AND COMMUNICATION

1 b; *2* a; *3* b

ETIQUETTE

2 bows; *3* ceremony; *4* avoid; *5* threatening

SOCIAL CONVENTIONS

1 a; *2* c; *3* a; *4* b; *5* b; *6* a; *7* a; *8* b; *9* a; *10* c

check your performance

TYPES OF ORGANISATION

2	MULTINATIONALS	*4*	LIMITED	*6*	MEDIUM
3	PUBLIC	*5*	CORPORATION		

PRESENT SIMPLE / PRESENT CONTINUOUS

2	belongs	*4*	is thinking	*6*	is changing
3	makes	*5*	thinks		

TELEPHONE LANGUAGE

2	cut off	*5*	hold on	*8*	up	*11*	collect
3	get through	*6*	busy	*9*	back		
4	hang up	*7*	afraid	*10*	leave		

SOCIAL SKILLS

2 d; *3* a; *4* f; *5* b; *6* c

2 the **company**

THE FOURTH LEAF OF THE SHAMROCK

1 We use our own private cars.
We put up our own kitchen cabinets.
We fill them in ourselves.
We draw out our own money from automatic cash tellers.

2 He predicts that restaurants may one day charge customers for cooking their own food.

WORD BUILDING

1	traditional	*4*	secretarial	*7*	administrative
2	successful	*5*	strategic	*8*	professional
3	flexible	*6*	challenging		

RESPONSIBILITIES

performance: keep an eye on; supervise; monitor; check
problems: solve; clear up; sort out; deal with
profits: increase; boost; stimulate; improve
people: manage; lead; oversee; be in charge of

FOCUS ON COMPANIES

On the recording:
The bid is friendly, not hostile.
The proposed merger won't take place.
CORDA made an increased offer of £250m.
The firm will be a significant presence in continental Europe.
Its US headquarters will be in Boston.
The job cuts will come in the UK and not in North America.

BUSINESS NEWS

as, reputable, electronics, old-fashioned, given, of, campaign, first, marketing, corporate, possibilities, directly, than, transform, name

OFFERS AND REQUESTS

2	I'm afraid	*5*	sit down	*7*	Do you mind if
3	Shall I	*6*	I'll have	*8*	Go ahead
4	Would you like				

BEING POLITE

2 I; *3* P; *4* I; *5* P; *6* I; *7* I; *8* I; *9* P; *10* P

MEETINGS

no; no; yes; yes; yes

WORD PARTNERS

pool resources	take the blame	hold a meeting
perform a task	make a decision	

check your **performance**

JOB DESCRIPTIONS

2	legal department	*5*	self-employed
3	computer programmer	*6*	chief executive officer
4	personnel manager		

OBLIGATION

2	don't have to	*4*	have to	*6*	has to
3	don't have to	*5*	mustn't		

MEETINGS

2	agenda	*4*	minutes	*6*	any other business
3	chairperson	*5*	brainstorm		

STARTING A MEETING

2	sort out this mess	*4*	lose $25,000
3	cancel our regional sales conference	*5*	set a time limit
		6	take the minutes

SOCIAL SKILLS

2	mind	*4*	sorry	*6*	all right
3	care	*5*	Excuse me		

3 **money**

MONEY MARKETS

junk bond	balance sheet
rights issue	venture capital
insider trading	capital gain
spot rate	

FINANCIAL NEWS

	MOVEMENT (+ OR −)	CLOSING PRICE
TSE-100 Index	+ 10.4	5211.6
Dow Jones Index	+ 12	8030
Associated Metals	− 5	426
RZT Group	+ 2	288
British Fuels	+ 4	208
WTC	+ 3	74
Courtman's	+ 1	55
GLX	+ 11	692
Smith & Parker	− 4	66
Transpax	+ 130	219
£ Sterling (\$ equivalent)	+ 1.4 − 3 pfennigs	\$ 1.57
International value (% of 1998 level)	+ 0.2%	88.9%

CURRENCIES

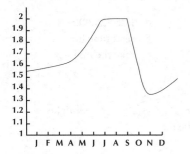

Japan: yen
India: rupee
Spain: peseta
China: yuan
Saudi Arabia: riyal
Italy/Turkey: lira
European Union: euro
Poland: zloty
Vietnam: dong
Mexico: peso
Brazil: cruzeiro
Greece: drachma
Russia: rouble
Thailand: baht

GRAPHS

CALCULATIONS

1 Gross profit = \$120 per packet
   Target sales = 50,000 packets
   50,000 × 120 = \$6m gross profit
   Less \$2.5m spent on advertising
   6 − 2.5 = 3.5m

2 Rent £7,415
   Wages £13,350
   Other overheads £60,050
   Total overheads £80,815

Year	Number of units sold	Variable costs (£10 per unit)	Fixed costs	Total costs	Sales income £15 per unit
1	3,000	30,000	22,500	52,500	45,000
2	6,000	60,000	22,500	82,500	90,000

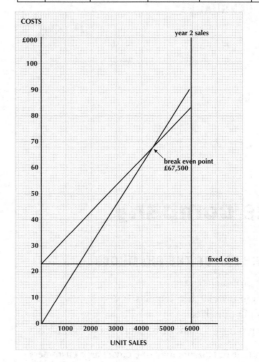

ACCOUNTING TERMS

2 current assets
3 debtors
4 current liabilities
5 creditors

SOCIAL SKILLS

2 c; 3 d; 4 g; 5 f; 6 a; 7 e

NUMBER PRONUNCIATION

1 a; 2 c; 3 c; 4 b; 5 a; 6 c

BREAKING THE ICE

2 h; 3 a; 4 d; 5 e; 6 g; 7 b; 8 f; 9 j; 10 i

TIME IS MONEY

to lose; to spend; to run out of; to waste

check your performance

OPPOSITES

profit – loss   assets – liabilities
bull – bear   boom – slump
creditor – debtor

THE LANGUAGE OF GRAPHS

1 e; 2 c; 3 b; 4 a; 5 d

PAST SIMPLE / PAST CONTINUOUS

2	were losing	7	encouraged
3	weren't investing	8	cut
4	weren't training	9	increased
5	became	10	closed down
6	restructured	11	had

FIGURES

2	£3,756	4	$^2/_3$	6	1,546,000
3	78.4%	5	C$12.6m		

the market

LAUNCHING A NEW PRODUCT

1

1

The five-year guarantee means that we believe in our product.
The water-resistant Coralon means that the camera won't get wet in a thunderstorm.
The reinforced stress points mean that the bag won't fall apart.
The protective padding means that the camera inside won't break if you drop the bag.

2

The 8Gb disk storage enables the user to store more data in the memory.
The voice navigation enables the user to give the computer oral instructions.
The 128K fax/modem enables the user to download data rapidly.
The plug-in module enables the user to add features to the previous model.
The on-site maintenance enables the user to call out technical support.
The ergonomic keyboard enables the user to type easily without getting tired.

2

The touch screen enables you to launch programs and enter data with a stylus pen.
The connecting cable enables you to move files to and from a desktop PC.
The compact size enables you to carry it around in your pocket.
The in-built digital voice recorder enables you to record fifteen minutes of messages.
The scheduler enables you to keep track of your appointments.

THE POST-IT® NOTE

2 a; *3* d; *4* c; *5* b; *6* c; *7* a; *8* c; *9* b; *10* d

SOUND AND SPELLING

1	count	3	coupon	5	brand
2	through	4	size		

ADVERTISING STYLES

1	luxurious	4	functional	7	masculine
2	humorous	5	caring	8	political
3	business-to-business	6	feminine		

A CIRCULAR LETTER

2	even	5	only slightly	7	enough
3	fully	6	convincingly	8	too good
4	highly				

MAKING AN ARRANGEMENT

2	wasn't it?	7	how about
3	I'm visiting	8	Let's
4	to fix a time	9	why don't we
5	are you coming	10	let's do that
6	can't make	11	look forward to seeing

ARRANGEMENTS

2	're attending	3	're visiting	4	're presenting

check your performance

ADVERTISING VOCABULARY

2	logo	4	campaign	6	campaign
3	sponsor	5	brand		

Hidden word is slogan

PRESENT PERFECT / PAST SIMPLE

2	took up	7	has used
3	has been	8	have you known
4	have not been	9	worked
5	has changed	10	has invested
6	launched	11	has grown

SOCIAL SKILLS

Making an excuse: 5; 11	Making an offer: 4; 7
Making an invitation: 1; 6; 9	Suggesting a date: 2; 3
Making an apology: 8; 10	

management

MANAGEMENT CULTURE

2	organisation	5	leadership	8	integrity
3	stamina	6	initiative	9	accountable
4	confident	7	judgement		

THEORY X AND THEORY Y

2 X; *3* Y; *4* Y; *5* X; *6* X; *7* Y

COPING WITH STRESS

3

1 F; *2* T

4

People will look after their own interests rather than those of the firm they work for.

Co-operation and team work will become even more difficult.

OXFORD BUSINESS BRIEFS

1

1 F; United States
2 T
3 F; It's hard to know in advance
4 T

2

1 Oxford Business Briefs are daily information to clients in international business.
2 Dr David Young and a team of specialists in Oxford.
3 Their major clients are big banks, oil companies, manufacturing multinationals.
4 Each of the briefs is divided into four parts: title, significance, analysis and conclusion.
5 Scott Walker finds them 40% useful and relevant, 35% marginal and 25% irrelevant to his needs.

WELCOMING A VISITOR

2 And where exactly are you staying?
3 How far away is it from here?
4 Did you walk here?
5 Would you like a seat?
6 How long are you staying in London?
7 Have you ever been there?
8 What's it like at this time of year?

CONVERSATIONS

2c; 3d; 4b; 5a

A JOB INTERVIEW

1 Why did you decide to leave TLM?
2 How long have you been in your present position?
3 How much do you earn at the moment?
4 How long did it take you to drive here?
5 How many candidates have you short-listed?
6 When did you become a public limited company?
7 How many people do you employ?
8 How much has your turnover increased by?
9 How often do you have a planning meeting?
10 Whose responsibility is staff development?

DEVELOPING A CONVERSATION

1 No, I don't think so.
2 Oh really! Well done!
3 Oh? Why not?
4 Yeah. You bet I do.
5 Right.
6 Mmm.
7 No. I see what you mean.

REPHRASING

1 efficient
2 effective
3 company man
4 globalisation
5 fallen dramatically
6 competitive
7 economies of scale
8 breakthrough
9 shakeout
10 gave in her notice

check your **performance**

QUESTIONS WITH *HOW*

2 How many people do they employ?
3 How many times did you speak to him?
4 How much do you expect to earn?
5 How far is the plant from the station?
6 How often do you have a planning meeting?

FUTURE

2	won't	*5*	will	*8*	will	*11*	won't
3	will	*6*	will	*9*	won't		
4	won't	*7*	will	*10*	will		

A JOB ADVERT

2 run
3 leading
4 track record
5 performance-related
6 benefits

WORD PARTNERS

research and development
mergers and acquisitions
supply and demand

carrot and stick
health and safety
terms and conditions

6 the **customer**

PRICES

1

1 rip-off
2 costly
3 reasonable
4 cheaply
5 giveaway
6 free

2

2 rip-off
3 costly
4 reasonable
5 cheaply
6 giveaway

IDIOMS

a bomb; the earth; an arm and a leg; a packet

TIMING A SALE

2 try a different approach before presenting it again.
3 don't try to force a commitment out of him/her after several weeks.

4 you need time to pass between the customer's request and your solution.

5 the customer will wonder how you managed to provide an individualised response so quickly.

6 the client will wait and be pleased to hear your proposals.

7 you can always call back straight away.

WORD PARTNERS

1 price; *2* decision; *3* demand; *4* market

THE ART OF PERSUASION

2

A good salesperson finds out what the customer wants to buy.
To make a sale you need to get the customer on your side.
A salesperson should be a good psychologist.

BARGAINING

PROPOSAL	COUNTER PROPOSAL

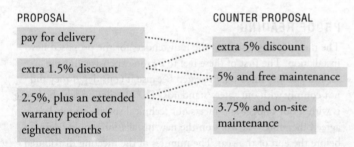

pay for delivery

extra 1.5% discount

2.5%, plus an extended warranty period of eighteen months

extra 5% discount

5% and free maintenance

3.75% and on-site maintenance

WORD PARTNERS

export sales
revenue sales
home sales
retail sales

sales car
sales technique
sales figures
sales forecast

FOOD AND DRINK

Spices: cinnamon, ginger, curry
Vegetables: cabbage, spinach, cauliflower
Meat: liver, lamb, pork
Fruit: apricot, pear, cherry
Seafood: lobster, shrimp, prawn
Types of drink: still, dry, sparkling
Ways of cooking: roast, bake, fry
Taste: bitter, spicy, sour
Cutlery: knife, fork, spoon

SPONSORSHIP

Sample report:

I have received three requests for sponsorship. After studying them carefully and making additional enquiries I feel that we should use the £500,000 earmarked for sponsorship on Susan Forster.

I believe she has great potential and is certainly going to be a major player on the international tennis circuit. Many people think she could be a future Wimbledon champion.

I feel that her endorsement of our sportswear and the expected

media coverage will give us an excellent opportunity of making our brand a household name.

check your **performance**

VOCABULARY

2 concede
3 lend
4 negotiate
5 offer
6 refuse

PAYMENT

2 e; *3* c; *4* f; *5* a; *6* d

CONDITIONALS

2 a; *3* b; *4* e; *5* f; *6* d

MORE CONDITIONALS

3 'll negotiate
4 goes
5 changed
6 wouldn't agree
7 offered

FOOD AND DRINK

2 e; *3* f; *4* a; *5* d; *6* b

7 production

PROJECT TEAMWORK

1

2 training
3 standard
4 ensure
5 brief
6 set up
7 smoothes
8 stage

2

2 THE FORMER METHOD: A SEQUENTIAL PROCESS
3 THE SPECIALISTS TAKE OVER
4 THE CHAIN OF COMMAND
5 EVEN SHORTER LEAD TIMES
6 MATRIX ORGANISATION

THE LEAN ENTERPRISE

Disadvantages:
It could never offer rewarding jobs to its employees and I think it's becoming evident that it could not also offer rewarding jobs to engineers either.
And it has become clear in recent years that mass production can also not attain high levels of quality.

1 check performance and quality
2 change the reporting structure and allow more authority and lower levels of the management structure
3 have a matrix organisation
4 set a good example for others to follow

WORD BUILDING

2	productivity	4	committed	6	operator
3	productive	5	commitment	7	operational

A COMPANY REPORT

1

a highly competitive market – reduced price tags

improved productivity – reduced wages and lower overheads

investment in new stores and extensions – higher capital
   expenditure than previously

boom in consumer spending – sales growth of 8.9%

better supply system – more products on the shelves

better buying and more efficient sourcing – a very small reduction
   in gross margins

an automatic warehouse – fewer items in stock

2

on account of; has meant; As a result of; Consequently; has led to;
due to

VERBS OF RESULT

1	results in	2	stemmed from	3	resulted in

PUTTING IT IN WRITING

2

It has come to my attention that a number of employees are failing
to comply with safety procedures. Operatives have been observed
without protective clothing and taking dangerous risks in order to
maintain the rate of production. Unless preventive measures are
taken swiftly, a serious injury will be inevitable.

MIXING BUSINESS WITH PLEASURE

(Sample answers)

1   I would avoid this as the ethnic restaurants are unlikely to serve
    food in the same way as they are used to in their own country.
    Secondly, part of the attraction of travel is tasting a different
    cuisine.

2   I would not personally as I wish to separate business from
    private life. But some people think that entertaining a business
    visitor in your own home is the best way to cement close
    relationships.

3   a   Pork is forbidden, as are forms of pork such as bacon, ham
        or sausage or any other foods cooked using the fat from
        pork products. Food should not be cooked in alcohol.
    b   Meat.
    c   Pork or shellfish. 'Kosher meat' and poultry may be eaten,
        if the animal has been killed in the correct way.

4   b   the main dish

5   b   you have had enough

TOPICS OF CONVERSATION

1	food	4	economics
2	family	5	sport
3	tourist attractions		

check your **performance**

PRODUCING TO ORDER

2	delivery	4	'just-in-time'	6	specifications
3	demand	5	logistics		

COMPOUND NOUNS

quality control   team leader   assembly line
work station   shop floor

CAUSES AND EFFECTS

2	as a result of	4	led to	6	as a result of
3	led to	5	as a result of		

DESCRIBING A PROCESS

2	is placed	4	complete	6	is made
3	are sent	5	are short-listed		

PROOF READING

The meeting <u>was discussed</u> the four tenders for the proposed new
installation. The first of these <u>feel</u> to be too expensive and the
second and the third were rejected because it <u>considered</u> they did
not comply with our safety standards. The installation which <u>choose</u>
is within our budget and meets our technical specifications. It
<u>agreed</u> therefore that work on the new installation would begin
before the end of the year. The minutes of the meeting <u>distributed</u>
to the shareholders.

2	was felt	4	was chosen	6	were distributed
3	was considered	5	was agreed		

8 business and society

ECONOMICS AND SOCIETY

2	so	5	those	7	to
3	that	6	such	8	if
4	their				

COLLOCATIONS

2	balance	4	means	6	standard
3	product	5	round		

DEDUCTIONS

1   This can't be about Anita Roddick. It must be about Richard
    Branson.

2   This can't be about Ted Turner. It must be about Bill Gates.

3   This can't be about Richard Branson. It must be about Ted
    Turner.

4   This can't be about Bill Gates. It must be about Akio Morita.

5   This can't be about Akio Morita. It must be about Anita
    Roddick.

MORE DEDUCTIONS

1 must have got	*4* can't have been
2 can't have read	*5* must have known
3 must have copied	*6* must have been

SPECULATING

(Suggested answers)

2 The factory must be polluting the river.
3 There must be a problem with that model.
4 They must be on strike.
5 They must be having an affair.

PRESENTATIONS

2 B; *3* J; *4* G; *5* A; *6* H; *7* I; *8* C; *9* D; *10* E

MAKING A PRESENTATION

1

2 However	*4* So	*6* whereas
3 Although	*5* In my opinion	*7* therefore

3

1 on the whole	*4* Now	*7* consequently
2 Even so	*5* To my mind	

EMPLOYMENT IN EUROPE

(Sample presentation)

As you can see from the graph, employment in the European Union has followed a similar pattern to North America with significant increases in unemployment as a result of the effects of the first oil crisis in the mid-1970s and again at the beginning of the 1980s.

If we compare countries in Europe and Scandinavia, we see that some countries have resisted better than others. In particular, richer nations such as Denmark, Germany, Luxembourg and Austria were able to keep youth unemployment as a proportion of the total active population at 10% or below. On the other hand, the number of young people deprived of a job reached alarming proportions in countries such as Spain, Italy or Finland and the European average of over 21% was unacceptably high.

Europe has also suffered from chronic long-term unemployment with, as you can see from the map, very high levels of long-term unemployment in the Iberian peninsula, Ireland, Italy and Greece. In this context, the French experience has been interesting with the intervention of Socialist governments in an attempt to create jobs by reducing the length of the working week to 35 hours. However, the connection between working hours and unemployment is by no means clear. Britain, with relatively low unemployment, has the longest working week in Europe.

RESPONDING TO INVITATIONS

Dear Mr Coleman

Thank you very much for your invitation to the Lions Club banquet on 14 December. I would be delighted to attend.

Yours sincerely

David Wheeler

Dear Carl,

Thanks for the invitation to the barbecue. It'll be great to see you both again after such a long time.

I'll bring some maps of Nepal with me.

Love
Mona

check your **performance**

ECONOMICS

1 economics	*4* economical
2 economic	*5* economist
3 economy	

PRESENTATIONS

2 e; *3* f; *4* b; *5* c; *6* a

ECONOMIC ORGANISATION

1 A; *2* D; *3* A; *4* A; *5* D; *6* D; *7* A; *8* D; *9* A; *10* D

DEDUCTIONS

1 can't	*3* must	*5* must
2 must	*4* can't	

A THANK YOU LETTER

2 last week	*4* put me up	*6* each other
3 hearing	*5* to have	

9 business ethics

SPECULATING ABOUT THE PAST

1 had known; wouldn't have invested; must have foreseen
2 had told; would have removed; must have realised
3 must have been; had informed; wouldn't have sold

LEARNING FROM THE PAST

1 c; *2* b; *3* b

CHILD LABOUR

2

1 Overseas suppliers are criticised because they employ children in unhealthy working conditions and at very low rates of pay.
2 Because this could cause further poverty.
3 It recommends tough rules to make sure overseas suppliers pay adequate wages, offer basic employment rights and do not employ children. It also suggests that companies should employ independent inspectors to make manufacturers respect their code of conduct.
4 80%

5 (Sample answer) The code of conduct probably contains some of the features recommended by Cafod but they are certainly not enforced properly.

3

1 highlights	*4* lodging	*6* deplored
2 boycott	*5* booming	*7* toughening
3 lay down		

CHILD LABOUR IN BRITAIN

1 underpaid, illegal and dangerous
2 is under thirteen, is supposed to be at school or works for more than two hours at a time.
3 children working on farms, selling flowers or cleaning car windscreens in the street

1 And what kind of work is it?
2 But why do young people do these jobs?
3 So why do I feel concerned?

WRITING

2

(Sample answer)

Dear Sir/Madam

I would like to point out, via your columns, that the recent criticism of our employment in the Third World is totally unjustified.

First of all, it is not company policy to employ children under fourteen. All our local personnel managers are instructed to use rigorous inspection procedures to identify any children under that age despite the lack of birth certificates in some areas. This requirement is clearly stated in the code of conduct.

Secondly, critics fail to take into account the fact that the employment of young people is deeply rooted in the culture of many developing countries. In those cases where we do employ young people, we provide free meals at the workplace. As a result, many of these people avoid the terrible effects of malnutrition and the money they earn is vital for supporting the whole family.

It is too easy to find fault with the employment policies of multinationals such as ours but there is a real danger of imposing Western values on other countries which have their own ideas of what is right or wrong. It should also be remembered that employment in a factory is, for many, a privilege and certainly a much better alternative than street crime or being sold into prostitution.

Yours faithfully

USING RHETORIC

1

T; F; T; F

2

Sound repetition
    picks up dirt, pins and pet hair, deep down clean. Be good to yourself. Be good to your home.

Exaggeration
    the world's undisputed Number 1. Millions of people ...
Parallels
    no fuss, no electricity, no noise, no cables to trip over, no disposable bags to replace, no accessories to lose
Superlatives
    the lightest, most efficient sweeper you can buy, the less effort you use, the more effectively it cleans

GREED IS BAD

2

1 Differences in colleagues' salaries may be a cause of disruption.
2 She couldn't believe she was being asked to do this.
3 No, it was lower.

3

an employee's previous experience
an employee's dynamism and creativity

check your **performance**

ETHICAL VOCABULARY

2 unfair	*4* indecent	*6* illegal
3 dishonest	*5* immoral	

THIRD CONDITIONAL

2 If they had listened to the union demands, there wouldn't have been a strike.
3 If we hadn't introduced job rotation, people wouldn't have learnt different skills.
4 If she hadn't had a headache, her presentation wouldn't have been poor.
5 If he hadn't bribed a ministry official, he wouldn't have got the contract.
6 If we hadn't increased our prices, we wouldn't have lost market share.

PRESENTATIONS

2 c; *3* b; *4* f; *5* a; *6* e

INVITATIONS AND OFFERS

Invitations and offers: 5, 6, 9, 10

Acceptances: 2, 3, 4

Refusals: 7, 8, 11

GIVING GIFTS

2 C; *3* D; *4* B; *5* F; *6* E